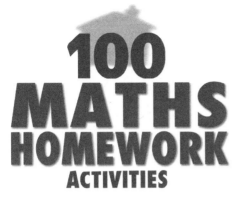

100 MATHS HOMEWORK ACTIVITIES

CONTENTS

G000042979

Published by
Scholastic Ltd,
Villiers House,
Clarendon Avenue,
Leamington Spa,
Warwickshire CV32 5PR

© Scholastic Ltd 2001
Text © Ann Montague-Smith 2001
4 5 6 7 8 9   4 5 6 7 8 9 0

AUTHOR
Ann Montague-Smith

EDITORIAL & DESIGN
Crystal Presentations Ltd

COVER DESIGN
Joy Monkhouse

ILLUSTRATOR
Theresa Tibbetts

Acknowledgements

The publishers wish to thank:
The Controller of HMSO and the DfEE for the use
of extracts from *The National Numeracy Strategy:
Framework for Teaching Mathematics* © March 1999,
Crown Copyright (1999, DfEE, Her Majesty's Stationery
Office).

British Library Cataloguing-in-Publication Data

A catalogue record of this book is available from the British
Library.

ISBN 0-439-01844-7

The right of Ann Montague-Smith to be identified as the
Author of this work has been asserted by her in accordance
with the Copyright, Designs and Patents Act 1988.

PAGE IN THIS BOOK	100 MATHS HOMEWORK ACTIVITIES YEAR 1		NATIONAL NUMERACY STRATEGY		100 MATHS LESSONS		
	ACTIVITY NAME	HOMEWORK TYPE	STRAND	TOPIC	NNS UNIT	LESSON	PAGE
29	Counting	Maths to share	Numbers and the number system	Counting and properties of numbers	1	2	21 22
30	Counters	Maths to share	Numbers and the number system	Counting and properties of numbers	1	2 3	22 23
31	Numeral snap	Maths to share	Numbers and the number system	Place value and ordering	2	1	26 27
32	Number track	Games and puzzles	Numbers and the number system	Place value and ordering	2	2	27 28
33	Making sums	Games and puzzles	Calculations	Understanding addition and subtraction; Mental calculations	2	3	28
34	Coin recognition	Maths to share	Solving problems	Problems involving money	3	6	30
35	Shopping	Games and puzzles	Solving problems	Problems involving money	3	8	31 32
36	5 and a bit	Maths to share	Calculations	Understanding addition and subtraction	3	9 10	32 33
37	Matching pair	Maths to share	Numbers and the number system	Place value and ordering	4	11	33
38	Tens and ones	Games and puzzles	Numbers and the number system	Place value and ordering	4	12 13	33 34
39	7p problem	Games and puzzles	Solving problems	Problems involving money	4	14 15	34 35
40	Longer and shorter	Maths to share	Measures, shape and space	Measures	5	1	40
41	Picture ruler	Games and puzzles	Measures, shape and space	Measures	5	3 4	42 43
42	Shape search	Maths to share	Measures, shape and space	Shape and space	6	5 6	43 44
43	Build a model	Games and puzzles	Measures, shape and space	Shape and space	6	7	45
44	Build a tower	Games and puzzles	Measures, shape and space	Shape and space	6	8	45
45	Number rhymes	Maths to share	Numbers and the number system	Counting and properties of numbers	8	1 3	52 53
46	Picture count	Maths to share	Numbers and the number system	Counting and properties of numbers	8	2 3	52 53
47	Number add	Games and puzzles	Solving problems	Reasoning about numbers	8	2 4	52 53
48	Pick up 15	Maths to share	Numbers and the number system	Estimating	9	1	57 58
49	Hand number	Maths to share	Numbers and the number system	Place value and ordering	9	2 3	58 59
50	Dice throw	Maths to share	Calculations	Understanding addition and subtraction; Mental calculations	9	5	60 61
51	Fruit shopping	Games and puzzles	Calculations	Understanding addition and subtraction; Mental calculations	10	5 6	60 61
52	Double or double add one	Maths to share	Calculations	Understanding addition and subtraction; Mental calculations	10	7 8	62 63
53	Take away	Games and puzzles	Calculations	Understanding addition and subtraction; Mental calculations	10	9 10	63 64

PAGE IN THIS BOOK	ACTIVITY NAME	HOMEWORK TYPE	STRAND	TOPIC	NNS UNIT	LESSON	PAGES
54	Under the tub	Games and puzzles	Calculations	Understanding addition and subtraction	11	11	64
55	Giving change	Games and puzzles	Calculations; Solving problems	Understanding addition and subtraction; Problems involving money	11	11 / 13	64 / 65
56	Making 10p	Games and puzzles	Solving problems	Problems involving money; Making decisions	11	14 / 15	65 / 66
57	Sequencing	Maths to share	Measures, shape and space	Measures	12	1	73 / 74
58	Telling the time	Maths to share	Measures, shape and space	Measures	12	1 / 3	73 / 75
59	What can you do in 1 minute?	Maths to share	Measures, shape and space; Solving problems	Measures; Problems involving measures	12	4 / 5	75 / 76
60	Favourite fruits	Maths to share	Solving problems	Organising and using data	13	6 / 7	76 / 77
61	Comparing	Maths to share	Measures, shape and space	Measures	13	8 / 10	77 / 78
62	How tall is a chair?	Games and puzzles	Measures, shape and space; Solving problems	Measures; Organising and using data	13	8 / 10	77 / 78
63	Odds and evens	Maths to share	Numbers and the number system	Counting and properties of numbers	1	1 / 2	87 / 88
64	Decade number search	Maths to share	Numbers and the number system	Counting and properties of numbers	1	1 / 3	87 / 88
65	Grid cover	Maths to share	Numbers and the number system	Place value and ordering	2	1 / 2	92 / 93
66	10 more, 10 less	Maths to share	Numbers and the number system	Place value and ordering	2	3 / 4	93 / 94
67	Counter toss	Games and puzzles	Calculations	Understanding addition and subtraction	2 / 3	5 / 6	95 / 96
68	Difference of 6	Games and puzzles	Calculations	Understanding addition and subtraction	2 / 3	5 / 7	95 / 96
69	Prices	Games and puzzles	Solving problems	Problems involving money	3	8 / 9	96 / 97
70	Shopping	Maths to share	Solving problems; Calculations	Problems involving money; Understanding addition and subtraction	3	10	98
71	8p	Games and puzzles	Solving problems; Calculations	Understanding addition and subtraction; Problems involving money	4	10 / 11	98 / 99
72	Totals 10	Games and puzzles	Calculations	Understanding addition and subtraction	4	10 / 12	98 / 99
73	Stamps	Games and puzzles	Solving problems	Problems involving money	4	13 / 15	100
74	Food comparison	Maths to share	Measures, shape and space	Measures	5	1 / 2	104 / 105
75	Weighing	Maths to share	Measures, shape and space	Measures	5	1 / 3	104 / 106
76	About the same	Maths to share	Solving problems	Problems involving measures	5	4	106 / 107
77	Shape pattern	Maths to share	Measures, shape and space	Shape and space	5 / 6	5 / 6	107 / 108

	100 MATHS HOMEWORK ACTIVITIES YEAR 1		NATIONAL NUMERACY STRATEGY		100 MATHS LESSONS		
PAGE IN THIS BOOK	ACTIVITY NAME	HOMEWORK TYPE	STRAND	TOPIC	NNS UNIT	LESSON	PAGE
78	Half a shape	Maths to share	Measures, shape and space	Shape and space	6	7	109
79	Jigsaw	Games and puzzles	Solving problems	Reasoning about shapes	6	8	110
80	Odd or even snap	Maths to share	Numbers and the number system	Counting and properties of numbers	8	1	118, 119
81	Counting pictures	Maths to share	Numbers and the number system	Counting and properties of numbers	8	1, 3	118, 120
82	Adding	Games and puzzles	Solving problems	Reasoning about numbers	8	4, 5	120, 121
83	Sports day	Maths to share	Numbers and the number system	Place value and ordering	9	1	124, 125
84	Comparing and ordering numbers	Games and puzzles	Numbers and the number system	Place value and ordering	9	2, 3	125, 126
85	Addition patterns for 13	Maths to share	Calculations	Mental calculations	9	4, 5	126, 127
86	Addition grid	Maths to share	Calculations	Mental calculations	10	6	128
87	Trio cards	Maths to share	Calculations	Understanding addition and subtraction	10	7	128
88	Three number addition	Maths to share	Calculations	Understanding addition and subtraction	10	7, 8	129
89	Favourite outings	Maths to share	Solving problems	Organising and using data	11	1	136
90	Marble grab	Maths to share	Solving problems	Organising and using data	11	1, 2	136
91	Time sheet	Maths to share	Measures, shape and space	Measures	11	4, 5	138, 139
92	Days of the week	Maths to share	Measures, shape and space	Measures	12	4, 6	138, 139
93	Hand span measure	Games and puzzles	Solving problems	Problems involving measures	12	7, 10	139, 140
94	About a kilogram	Games and puzzles	Solving problems	Problems involving measures	12	7, 10	139, 140
95	Counting many shapes	Maths to share	Numbers and the number system	Counting and properties of numbers	1	1	149, 150
96	What comes next?	Games and puzzles	Numbers and the number system	Counting and properties of numbers	1	1, 3	149, 151
97	Missing numbers	Games and puzzles	Numbers and the number system	Place value and ordering	2	1, 2	156, 157
98	Counter moves	Games and puzzles	Numbers and the number system	Place value and ordering	2	3, 2	157, 158
99	Card add	Maths to share	Calculations	Understanding addition and subtraction; Mental calculations	2, 3	5, 6	159
100	Bridging 10	Maths to share	Calculations	Mental calculations in addition and subtraction	3	7	160
101	Change from 20p	Maths to share	Solving problems; Calculations	Problems involving money; Understanding addition and subtraction; Mental calculations	3	7, 9	160, 161
102	Total 14	Games and puzzles	Calculations	Mental calculations in addition and subtraction	3	10	161, 162
103	Addition sums	Games and puzzles	Calculations	Mental calculations in addition and subtraction	4	11	162

PAGE IN THIS BOOK	ACTIVITY NAME	HOMEWORK TYPE	STRAND	TOPIC	NNS UNIT	LESSON	PAGES
104	Subtraction sums	Games and puzzles	Calculations	Mental calculations in addition and subtraction	4	12 / 13	162 / 163
105	Total 20p	Games and puzzles	Solving problems	Problems involving money	4	14 / 15	163 / 164
106	Water fun	Maths to share	Measures, shape and space	Measures	5	2	171
107	Capacity comparison	Maths to share	Solving problems	Problems involving measures	5	2 / 3	171 / 172
108	Picture these	Maths to share	Measures, shape and space	Shape and space	5 / 6	5 / 6	173 / 174
109	Colour pattern	Maths to share	Measures, shape and space	Shape and space	6	5 / 7	172 / 174
110	Find the way home	Games and puzzles	Solving problems	Reasoning about shapes	6	5 / 8	172 / 174
111	Number pattern board game	Games and puzzles	Numbers and the number system	Counting and properties of numbers	8	2	181 / 182
112	Number patterns	Games and puzzles	Numbers and the number system	Counting and properties of numbers	8	2 / 3	181 / 182
113	Making 19	Games and puzzles	Solving problems	Reasoning about numbers	8	4 / 5	182 / 183
114	Ordering to 20	Games and puzzles	Numbers and the number system	Place value and ordering	9	1 / 2	186 / 187
115	Counter count	Maths to share	Numbers and the number system	Estimating	9	3	187 / 188
116	Where does it fit?	Maths to share	Numbers and the number system	Place value and ordering	9	4 / 5	188 / 189
117	Number cover up	Games and puzzles	Calculations	Mental calculations in addition and subtraction	10	6 / 7	189 / 190
118	Box add	Games and puzzles	Calculations	Mental calculations in addition and subtraction	10	8 / 9	191
119	Totals	Games and puzzles	Calculations	Mental calculations in addition and subtraction	10	10	192
120	Giving change	Maths to share	Solving problems	Problems involving money	11	11 / 12	192 / 193
121	Totalling 19	Games and puzzles	Solving problems	Reasoning about numbers	11	13 / 14	193 / 194
122	Paying 18p	Games and puzzles	Solving problems	Problems involving money	11	13 / 15	193 / 194
123	Measuring capacity	Maths to share	Measures, shape and space	Measures	12	1 / 2	201 / 202
124	Time order	Maths to share	Measures, shape and space	Measures	12	3 / 4	202 / 203
125	The week and the seasons	Maths to share	Measures, shape and space	Measures	12	3 / 5	202 / 203
126	About me	Maths to share	Solving problems	Problems involving measures	13	6 / 7	204
127	How many?	Maths to share	Solving problems	Organising and using data	13	8 / 10	205
128	What can we tell?	Maths to share	Solving problems	Organising and using data	13	8 / 10	205

100 MATHS HOMEWORK ACTIVITIES

100 Maths Homework Activities is a series of teachers' resource books for Years 1–6. Each book is year-specific and provides a core of homework activities for mathematics within the guidelines for the National Numeracy Strategy in England. The content of these activities is also appropriate for and adaptable to the requirements of Primary 1–7 in Scottish schools.

Each book offers three terms of homework activities, matched to the termly planning in the National Numeracy Strategy *Framework for Teaching Mathematics* for that year. Schools in England and Wales that decide not to adopt the National Numeracy Strategy will still find the objectives, approaches and lesson contexts familiar and valuable. However, the teacher will need to choose from the activities to match their own requirements and planning.

The homework activities provided in the books are intended as a support for the teacher, school mathematics leader or trainee teacher. The series can be used alongside its companion series, *100 Maths Lessons and more*, or with any mathematics scheme of work, as the basis for planning homework activities throughout the school, in line with the school's homework policy. The resources can be used by teachers with single-age classes, mixed-age, single- and mixed-ability groups and for team planning of homework across a year or key stage. The teacher may also find the activities valuable for extension work in class or as additional resources for assessment.

Using the books

The activities in this book are for Year 1/Primary 1–2 classes and are a mix of mathematics to share with a helper – a parent, neighbour or sibling – and games and puzzles to do at home. For Years 2–6/Primary 2–7, there are also practice exercises, some 'against the clock', and activities to help the children develop mathematics investigation skills. The activities have been chosen to ensure that each strand and topic of the National Numeracy Strategy *Framework for Teaching Mathematics* is included and that the children have opportunities to develop their mental strategies, use paper-and-pencil methods appropriately, and use and apply their mathematics to solve problems.

Each of the 100 homework activities in this book includes a photocopiable page to send home. The page provides instructions for the child and a brief explanation for a helper, stating simply and clearly its purpose and suggesting support and/or a further challenge to offer the child. The mathematics strand and topic addressed by each activity and the type of homework being offered are indicated on each page. The types are shown by the following symbols:

 maths to share

 games and puzzles

 practice exercise

 investigation

 timed practice exercise

There is a supporting teacher's note for each activity. These notes include:

- **Learning outcomes:** the specific learning objectives of the homework (taken from the National Numeracy Strategy *Framework for Teaching Mathematics*);

- **Lesson context:** a brief description of the classroom experience recommended for the children prior to undertaking the homework activity;

- **Setting the homework:** advice on how to explain the work to the children and set it in context before it is taken home;

- **Back at school:** suggestions for how to respond to the returned homework, such as discussion with the children or specific advice on marking, as well as answers, where relevant.

Supporting your helpers

Extensive research by the IMPACT Project (based at University of North London) has demonstrated how important parental involvement is to children's success in mathematics. A photocopiable homework diary sheet is provided on page 8 which can be sent home with the homework. This sheet has room for records of four pieces of homework and can be kept singly in a file or multiple copies stapled together to make a longer-term homework record. For each activity, there is space to record its name and the date when it was sent home and spaces for responses to the work from the helper, the child and the teacher. The homework diary is intended to encourage home–school links, so that parents and carers know what is being taught and can make informed comments about their child's progress.

Name _____		Child's comments		Teacher's comments
Name of activity & date sent home	Helper's comments	Did you like this? Draw a face. ☺ a lot ☺ a little ☹ not much	How much did you learn? Draw a face. ☺ a lot ☺ a little ☹ not much	
PICTURE COUNT	JONATHAN DREW SOME OF HIS OWN PICTURES AND COUNTED THOSE CORRECTLY. I AM VERY PLEASED WITH THE WAY HE HAS IMPROVED IN HIS COUNTING.	☺	☺	Jonathan has made great progress. Encourage him to count things that he can't touch so that he remembers which he has counted and which are still to be counted.
PICK UP 15	WE PLAYED THIS GAME TOGETHER. JONATHAN FOUND THIS EASIER THAN I DID! I THINK HE IS BETTER AT	☺	☺	Jonathan was so pleased that he won! Have you tried increasing to 20 the number to be estimated?

Using the activities with *100 Maths Lessons* series

The organisation of the homework activities in this book matches the planning grids within *100 Maths Lessons and more: Year 1* (also written by Ann Montague-Smith and published by Scholastic), so that there is homework matching the learning objectives covered in each unit of work in each term. Grids, including details of which lessons in *100 Maths Lessons and more: Year 1* have associated homework activities in *100 Maths Homework Activities*, with the relevant page numbers, are provided on pages 2–5 in this book to help teachers using *100 Maths Lessons and more: Year 1* with their planning.

About this book: Year 1/Primary 1–2

This book contains two types of homework activities for children in Year 1/Primary 1–2: 'Maths to share' activities and 'Games and puzzles'.

'Maths to share' activities encourage the child and a helper to discuss and work together on the mathematics. These tasks draw heavily on the home context. The 'Puzzles' are investigations or problem-solving tasks through which the child can explore an aspect of mathematics, together with a helper, over a longer period of time, such as a week or a weekend. The 'Games' are for child and helper to play together.

Where there are specific solutions to these activities, it is recommended that these should be sent home at a later date.

Name _____

Name of activity & date sent home	Helper's comments	Child's comments		Teacher's comments
		Did you like this? Draw a face. ☺ a lot :| a little ☹ not much	**How much did you learn?** Draw a face. ☺ a lot :| a little ☹ not much	

100 MATHS HOMEWORK ACTIVITIES • YEAR 1 HOMEWORK DIARY

Teachers' notes

TERM 1

p29 COUNTING   MATHS TO SHARE

Learning outcomes
*   Know the number names and recite them in order to at least 20, from and back to zero.
*   Describe and extend number sequences: **count on and back in ones from any small number.**

Lesson context
Provide opportunities for the children to sing and say number rhymes. Count all together and around the class, in ones, forwards to 10, then to 20 and back to zero. Ask questions such as: *What is before/after...?* Encourage the children to count on and back in ones from any small number such as 2 or 3.

Setting the homework
Explain that there is a counting rhyme with actions on the sheet. Practise the actions with the children before they take the sheet home.

Back at school
Use this rhyme as part of an oral starter activity. Children sing the rhyme, then recite the numbers from zero to 10 and back again. Encourage the children to count rhythmically.

p30 COUNTERS   MATHS TO SHARE

Learning outcome
*   **Count reliably at least 10 objects.**

Lesson context
Children touch-count five to ten objects, moving each object as it is counted. This will help them to see what they have counted and what is still to be counted. Discuss how the last number that is said is also the number of objects.

Setting the homework
Demonstrate the activity. Using an enlarged copy of page 30 may be helpful. Take a small handful of counters, place them in the 'garden' drawn on the photocopiable sheet and count them.

Back at school
Ask the children to count out given amounts. Ask the children to check each other's counting, by swapping amounts and re-counting.

p31 NUMERAL SNAP   MATHS TO SHARE

Learning outcomes
*   **Read and write numerals from 0 to at least 20.**

Lesson context
Children make matching pairs of numerals. They read the numeral on a card. Ask them to hold up a card for the given numeral so that they can show which ones they recognise. Ask children to trace the number shapes with their fingers.

Setting the homework
Explain the game of snap to the children. If they do not have playing cards at home, loan a set of numeral cards or explain to the children how to make their own set.

Back at school
Play the snap game as a class. Ask a child to turn over a card on behalf of the class and you turn one over. Each time, encourage all the children to read both cards and decide whether they match or not.

p32 NUMBER TRACK   GAMES AND PUZZLES

Learning outcomes
*   **Read and write numerals from 0 to at least 20.**
*   **Order numbers to at least 20,** and position them on a number track.

Lesson context
Work with the children to order numbers by pegging large numeral and number word cards on to a washing line and reading both the numeral and the word. Using a number track, ask the children to count on from given numbers: *Start at 3; count on 2. What number have you reached? (5)* Check that the children count on from the first number, and do not count it as 'one'.

Setting the homework
Explain to the children that on each turn they must toss the dice twice: the first time tells them the starting number and the second time how many to count on.

Back at school
Play the game with the class. Make an A3 enlargement of the number track from photocopiable page 32. Invite a child to toss the dice for the start number and again for how many to count on. The class should check the count.

p33 MAKING SUMS   GAMES AND PUZZLES

Learning outcomes
*   **Understand the operation of addition, and use the related vocabulary.**
*   Put the larger number first, and count on in ones.

Lesson context
Practise combining two small numbers by putting the larger number first and counting on using a number line. When they are confident with this, encourage the children to repeat the activity, but this time counting on in their heads.

Setting the homework
Make sure that the children understand that they have to choose two from the four numbers on the sheet each time. They then use them to write an add sum in the recording box and then find the total and write that down.

Back at school
Mark the sums. Identify any children who had difficulty with this work. They may need further experience of adding using a printed number line until they are confident at using their 'mental number line.'

p34 COIN RECOGNITION

Learning outcome
- Recognise coins of different values.

Lesson context
Match coins and find equivalent values for 1p, 2p, 5p and 10p coins. Show the children how to find equivalent values by matching 1p coins to 2p, 5p and 10p, then extending this to other values less than 10p.

Setting the homework
Explain to the children that they are going to compare coins to match those that are worth the same and name them.

Back at school
Ask the children to find the coins that you name: *Show me a 5p coin… Now a coin worth more than 5p. What is it called?*

p35 SHOPPING

Learning outcome
- Recognise coins of different values.

Lesson context
Encourage the children to purchase items from the class shop costing up to 10p and pay for them with pennies. Ask them to find other ways of paying; for 4p: 1p +1p + 1p + 1p; or 1p + 1p + 2p; or 2p + 2p. Encourage the children to find which way uses the least number of coins.

Setting the homework
Explain the game to the children. They choose an item to buy and count out coins to pay for it, finding different combinations of coins to make the cost.

Back at school
Discuss how inconvenient it would be to pay for everything using pennies. Ask the children to use coins to find some amounts, such as 5p or 6p. Encourage the children to find different ways of doing this.

p36 5 AND A BIT

Learning outcomes
- **Understand the operation of addition and use the related vocabulary.**
- Begin to recognise that addition can be done in any order.
- Begin to use the + and = signs to record mental calculations in a number sentence, and to recognise the use of □ to stand for an unknown number.
- Begin to partition into 5 and a bit when adding 6, 7, 8 or 9, then recombine.

Lesson context
Let the children use rods or interlocking cubes to see how 6, 7, 8 or 9 can be partitioned into 5 and a bit when adding. They total the 5s, then count on in ones: for 5 + 6 this is: *5 and 5 is 10 and 1 more is 11.*

Setting the homework
Explain to the children that they need to spin a paperclip on the 'spinner' to determine the number and then say it as a '5 and a bit' number.

Back at school
Ask the children to break down numbers into '5 and a bit' as part of an oral and mental starter activity. Then ask the children to add the number to 5. Encourage them to say, for example, for 5 + 9: *5 and 5 is 10 and 4 is 14.*

p37 MATCHING PAIR

Learning outcomes
- **Read and write numerals from 0 to at least 20.**

Lesson context
Ask the children to match numeral and number word cards and read both, then order them on a washing line, first from zero to 10, then to 20.

Setting the homework
Explain to the children that the number and word cards on the homework sheet should be cut out when they get home so that they can play the game. Ask them to read each card that they turn over.

Back at school
Play the same Pelmanism game with the children by fixing enlarged versions of the cards to a board with Blu-Tack so that the backs of the cards show. Ask the children to take turns to choose two cards and get everyone to read each one. When a child finds a match, the cards are removed from the board.

p38 TENS AND ONES

Learning outcomes
- Begin to know what each digit in a two-digit number represents. Partition a 'teens' number and begin to partition larger two-digit numbers into a multiple of 10 and ones (TU).

Lesson context
Practise exchanging ones for a ten and units. Provide materials, such as straws, for bundling into a ten and ones, keeping the quantity to 20 or less each time.

Setting the homework
Explain the activity and demonstrate it, using 10p and 1p coins to represent a ten and ones.

Back at school
Ask the children to count out given quantities of pennies and to change them into a 10p and ones. For example, for 17p the children will count out 17 penny coins, then change these to a 10p and seven 1p coins.

p39 7p PROBLEM

Learning outcomes
- **Use mental strategies to solve simple problems** set in money contexts, **using counting, addition, subtraction, doubling and halving, explaining methods and reasoning orally.**

Lesson context
Work on some oral money problems, such as: *I want to buy an apple for 8p, which coins shall I use? I have 6p in my pocket, what coins might I have?* If the children have difficulty with working out these questions mentally, provide coins to help them.

Setting the homework
Explain that to solve the problem on the sheet only 1p, 2p and 5p coins can be used.

Back at school
Draw some large purse outlines on the flip chart and ask individual children to suggest a solution to the problem. Extend the problem by asking: *What if I had 9p in my pocket: what coins might I have? What would be the least number of coins that I could have?*

p40 LONGER AND SHORTER

MATHS TO SHARE

Learning outcomes
- **Compare two lengths by direct comparison**; extend to more than two.

Lesson context
Tell the children to compare two objects for length, then for width. Set some practical problems to be solved, such as: *Which is longer, my book or my shoe? Which is the narrowest ribbon in the box?* Discuss the children's solution strategies during a plenary session.

Setting the homework
Explain the activity and demonstrate if necessary.

Back at school
Review the sheets, checking that the children have drawn their toys in the appropriate boxes. Where there is evidence of misunderstanding, provide further opportunities to use the vocabulary of length in practical situations.

p41 PICTURE RULER
GAMES AND PUZZLES

Learning outcome
- **Suggest suitable standard or uniform non-standard units and measuring equipment to estimate, then measure, length,** recording estimates and measurements as 'about...'

Lesson context
Encourage the children to solve measuring problems using uniform non-standard units, such as estimating then measuring the length of their book. Encourage them to repeat this, using different non-standard units and to discuss their choice. Ask the children to record their estimates and their measures. Encourage them to recognise that their measurements are approximate by using words, such as, 'nearly' or 'about'.

Setting the homework
Explain the activity. Say that the children can cut out the picture ruler so that they can use it around their home.

Back at school
Discuss the range of objects measuring about 8 pictures in length. Ask the children to estimate objects in the classroom that are of about the same length and to check by measuring.

p42 SHAPE SEARCH

MATHS TO SHARE

Learning outcome
- **Use everyday language to describe features of familiar 3-D shapes,** including the cube, cuboid, sphere, cylinder, cone, referring to properties, such as the shapes of flat faces or the number of faces or corners.

Lesson context
Offer some activities for sorting and naming 3-D shapes and describing their properties. Ask the children to describe shapes, saying how many flat/curved faces and edges a shape has. At the end of the lesson, use a feely bag game with shapes hidden in a bag. Encourage the children to describe the shapes for others to guess the shapes' names.

Setting the homework
Explain the activity. Encourage the children to think of things at home which are cubes, cuboids and so on.

Back at school
Discuss the range of items that the children found and ask them to explain their shapes. Relate this to mathematical models of 3-D shapes.

p43 BUILD A MODEL

GAMES AND PUZZLES

Learning outcomes
- Make and describe models using construction kits, everyday materials, Plasticine...
- Begin to relate solid shapes to pictures of them.

Lesson context
Ask the children to copy pictures to make models. Provide a range of construction and malleable materials for the children to make models. During the plenary, discuss how the models are similar to, and different from, the pictures.

Setting the homework
Explain the task and tell the children that they can use construction kits or reclaimed materials to make their models. Emphasise that 'different' is 'OK'; to avoid complaints if LEGO is not available, for example.

Back at school
Discuss the models which were made. Some children may wish to bring their models into school, so these can be the focus of the discussion. Compare the models to the picture and discuss similarities and differences. Make a display of the drawings and models.

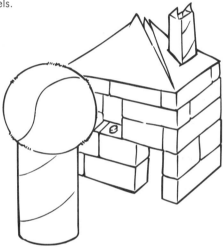

p44 BUILD A TOWER

GAMES AND PUZZLES

Learning outcomes
- Solve simple mathematical problems; recognise and predict from simple patterns and relationships. Suggest extensions by asking 'What if...?' or 'what could I try next?'

Lesson context
Ask the children to solve shape puzzles, such as using four interlocking cubes to make as many different shapes as they can find. Encourage the children to respond to: *What if...?* and *What could I try next?* questions as they work. During the plenary, ask individual children to describe their solutions so that others can make comparisons with their own.

Setting the homework
Explain the activity and that the children can use construction kits, malleable or reclaimed materials to make their model. Ask them to bring their pictures to school.

Back at school
Some children may bring their models to school. If so, compare the model and the picture and discuss similarities and differences between the picture and the model. Otherwise, choose a picture and, in front of the children, build the model that is shown and ask the children to discuss their similarities and differences.

p45 NUMBER RHYMES

MATHS TO SHARE

Learning outcomes
- Know the number names and recite them in order to at least 20, from and back to zero.
- Describe and extend number sequences: **count on and back in ones from any small number, and in tens from and back to zero.**

Lesson context
Together and around the class, count in ones from any small number and in tens from and back to zero. Use favourite number rhymes, then count rhythmically together, then around the class. Ask questions such as: *What comes before/next? Start on 3, count on 4, what number is that?* Count in tens using a class number line marked from 0 to 100 and point to the numbers as you count forwards and back to zero.

Setting the homework
Ask the children to think of some of their favourite number rhymes which they can teach to their helper. Explain that they will be counting in ones and tens.

Back at school
Say some of the children's favourite number rhymes for counting in ones. Ask individual children to count in ones from any small number and back to zero. Repeat this for counting in tens, from and back to zero.

p46 PICTURE COUNT

MATHS TO SHARE

Learning outcome
- **Count reliably at least 10 objects.**

Lesson context
Ask the children to count the objects in a picture by touching the items. Include the idea of zero by asking the children to count something that is not there.

Setting the homework
Explain the activity to the children. Explain that they can also draw their own counting pictures on the back of the sheet and write the numerals.

Back at school
Draw some spots on the flip chart and ask the children to count them. This time they will not be able to touch the pictures. Instead, encourage them to point and remember which spots they have already counted.

p47 NUMBER ADD

GAMES AND PUZZLES

Learning outcomes
- Solve simple mathematical problems or puzzles, recognize and predict from simple patterns and relationships. Suggest extensions by asking 'What if...?' or 'what could I try next?'
- Explain methods and reasoning orally.

Lesson context
Provide the children with some problems to solve by counting, such as using playing cards and counting the pips to make a given total. Encourage the children to respond to questions such as: *What if...?* or *What could I try next?*

Setting the homework
Explain the activity. Suggest to the children that before they begin, they count carefully how many items are in each box.

Back at school
Ask the children to give examples of ways of finding combinations for 16, using two boxes, then three. Write the responses as addition sentences on the flip chart.

p48 PICK UP 15

MATHS TO SHARE

Learning outcomes
- Understand and use the vocabulary of estimation.
- Give a sensible estimate of a number of objects which can be checked by counting.

Lesson context
Provide some Base 10 apparatus. Ask the children to take and estimate the number in a small quantity of unit cubes and then to exchange these for a ten and some ones. Ask the children to estimate how many cubes they think they have, encouraging them to make their estimates as accurate as possible as they experience checking by counting.

Setting the homework
Explain the activity and encourage the children to estimate the number before they count how many.

Back at school
Use a different material, such as coloured straws. Ask the children to estimate how many they think you have picked up, then encourage a child to check by counting.

p49 HAND NUMBER

MATHS TO SHARE

Learning outcomes
- Begin to know what each digit in a two-digit number represents. Partition a 'teens' number and begin to partition larger two-digit numbers into a multiple of 10 and ones (TU).

Lesson context
Use arrow cards and a paper abacus to practise representing tens and units numbers. Encourage the children to record TU numbers using extended form, for example, 15 = 10 + 5.

Setting the homework
Explain the activity and say that instead of counters the hand outline can be filled with other identical items such as 2p coins or buttons or small bricks.

Back at school
Ask individual children to write their TU numbers on the flip chart and to record in extended form: 18 = 10 + 8. Discuss the range of responses and ask: *Who had the largest hand?*

p50 DICE THROW

MATHS TO SHARE

Learning outcomes
- **Understand the operation of addition and use the related vocabulary.**
- Begin to recognise that addition can be done in any order.
- Begin to recognise that more than two numbers can be added together.
- Use knowledge that addition can be done in any order to do mental calculations more efficiently. For example, begin to partition into '5 and a bit' when adding 6, 7, 8 or 9, then recombine.

Lesson context
Ask the children to partition the numbers 6, 7, 8 or 9 into '5 and a bit' when adding. For example, for 5 + 8: 5 + 5 + 3 = 10 + 3 = 13. Encourage the children to use strategies such as counting on in ones or, for the lower ability, use a number line until they are more confident.

Setting the homework
Explain that the game is played like any board game with dice and counters to mark their place. Ask the children to use the partitioning strategy to solve the sums on the board.

Back at school
Make an A3 version of the homework sheet. Play the game against the class, encouraging the children to work quickly to solve each sum, using the partitioning strategy.

p51 FRUIT SHOPPING

GAMES AND PUZZLES

Learning outcomes
- **Understand the operation of addition and use the related vocabulary.**
- Begin to recognise that addition can be done in any order.
- Begin to recognise that more than two numbers can be added together.
- Use knowledge that addition can be done in any order to do mental calculations more efficiently. For example, begin to partition into '5 and a bit' when adding 6, 7, 8 or 9, then recombine.
- Recognise coins of different values.

Lesson context
Introduce the strategy of adding by partitioning and recombining with money totals, as well as with just numbers. Children can use coins to help them total the amounts, breaking the amounts into '5 and a bit'.

Setting the homework
Explain the activity and suggest to the children that they use money at home to help them solve the problems.

Back at school
Ask the children to suggest combinations to make a total of 15p.

p52 DOUBLE OR DOUBLE ADD ONE

MATHS TO SHARE

Learning outcomes
- **Understand the operation of addition and use the related vocabulary.**
- Begin to recognise that addition can be done in any order and that more than two numbers can be added together.
- Identify near doubles, using doubles already known, (e.g. 6 + 5).

Lesson context
Ask the children to use doubles facts to find near doubles. Where the children find this difficult, provide apparatus to help, such as interlocking cubes to make near double towers. Ask them to record their sums, for example, 4 + 4 = 8; or 4 + 5 = 4 + 4 + 1 = 9, and discuss how doubles can be used to find near doubles.

Setting the homework
Explain the activity. Explain that if the children do not have playing cards at home, they can make their own 1–10 cards using any scrap paper or card.

Back at school
Use the activity on the homework sheet as an oral and mental starter activity, encouraging the children to use their doubles facts to work out near doubles.

p53 TAKE AWAY

GAMES AND PUZZLES

Learning outcomes
- **Understand the operation of subtraction (as 'take away') and use the related vocabulary.**
- Use patterns of similar calculations.

Lesson context
Demonstrate subtraction as 'take away' by using towers of interlocking cubes, taking away the smaller amount. Record the subtractions on the flip chart, 7 – 3 = 4. Encourage the children to find all the subtractions for a given starting number, such as: 6 – 0; 6 – 1; 6 – 2 and so on.

Setting the homework
Explain that the children should pick two of the numbers each time and write their own subtractions. Remind them that when doing subtractions they write the larger number first, 7 – 2.

Back at school
Review some of the subtractions that individual children wrote, asking the others to work out the answers mentally.

p54 UNDER THE TUB

GAMES AND PUZZLES

Learning outcome
- **Understand the operation of subtraction** (as 'how many more to make') **and use the related vocabulary.**

Lesson context
Demonstrate the subtraction strategy of complementary addition by counting on in ones from the smaller to the larger number. Encourage the children to use this strategy to solve problems involving, 'how many more to make…'.

Setting the homework
Explain the activity and that this is a puzzle which has a number of different answers.

Back at school
Ask the children to take turns to give an example of a 'how many more to make 8?' sum and write these as subtractions on the flip chart.

p55 GIVING CHANGE

GAMES AND PUZZLES

Learning outcomes
- **Understand the operation of subtraction** (as 'how many more to make') **and use the related vocabulary.**
- Find totals and change from 10p.

Lesson context
Ask the children to use the subtraction strategy of complementary addition when giving change. Encourage them to count on in their heads in ones from the lower price to the amount tendered, to find the change.

Setting the homework
Explain that this can be done using money to count out the change.

Back at school
During oral and mental maths time, ask the children some money word problems, such as: I buy an orange for 7p and give a 10p coin: how much change will I have?

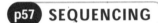

p56 MAKING 10P   GAMES AND PUZZLES

Learning outcomes
- **Use mental strategies to solve simple problems** set in 'real life' or money contexts, **using counting, addition, subtraction, doubling and halving, explaining methods and reasoning orally.**
- Choose and use appropriate number operations and mental strategies to solve problems.

Lesson context
Provide some problems set in 'real life' and money contexts for the children to solve. Put out coins for the children to use to solve the money problems until they are confident enough with their mental strategies to solve them without the coins.

Setting the homework
Explain the activity to the children and ask them to write their answers as addition sums. Explain that they may find it helpful to use coins to solve the problems.

Back at school
Mark the work. If further practice is required, use the activity as part of an oral and mental starter, making amounts for 9p, 12p and so on.

p57 SEQUENCING   MATHS TO SHARE

Learning outcomes
- Understand and use the vocabulary related to time.
- Order familiar events in time.

Lesson context
Ask the children to sequence events. Encourage them to talk about their day and put events in time order. Link this to reading the time to the hour on analogue clocks.

Setting the homework
Explain that the pictures on the sheet are out of order and need to be cut out and stuck on another sheet of paper in the order that the events happened.

Back at school
Review the homework activity with the children using an A3 enlargement of the homework sheet for them to order the pictures. Encourage the children to give reasons for their ordering of these events. Discuss some of the children's own drawings.

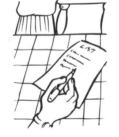

p58 TELLING THE TIME   MATHS TO SHARE

Learning outcomes
- Understand and use the vocabulary related to time.
- Read the time to the hour or half-hour on analogue clocks.

Lesson context
Encourage the children to set the hands on cardboard clocks to the times which you give them. Begin with o'clock times and then introduce 'half-past'. Encourage them to note the differences between the two clock hands so that they can tell them apart.

Setting the homework
Explain the activity to the children. Decide whether they should take home a cardboard clock face to use with the homework or whether to ask helpers if the children can use a real clock.

Back at school
Enlarge a copy of the homework sheet to A3 and discuss the pictures and the times they represent. Ask the children to set their clock faces to the o'clock and half-past times that you give them.

p59 WHAT CAN YOU DO IN 1 MINUTE?   MATHS TO SHARE

Learning outcomes
- Understand and use the vocabulary related to time.
- **Use mental strategies to solve simple problems** set in measurement contexts, **using counting, addition, subtraction, doubling and halving, explaining methods and reasoning orally.**

Lesson context
Use sand-timers, stop-watches, water-clocks and so on for the children to measure given amounts of time. Ask the children to carry out activities such as skipping or doing up their shoe laces for a given amount of time. Encourage them to estimate how many first, then to measure.

Setting the homework
Explain that you would like the children to try some activities at home, and that each one should take one minute in time. Say that the children will need a clock or watch with a second hand so that they can measure one minute.

Back at school
Ask the children to shut their eyes and keep them shut for their estimate of a minute. Discuss their estimation strategies.

p60 FAVOURITE FRUITS   MATHS TO SHARE

Learning outcome
- Solve a given problem by sorting, classifying and organizing information in simple ways, such as in a list or simple table. Discuss and explain results.

Lesson context
Provide opportunities for children to sort items by colour, size, shape and by quantity and to record their sorting in a list. Discuss the results of the sorting, asking questions such as: *Which has most/least? How many in total?* The results can be put into a simple table.

Setting the homework
Explain that you would like the children to collect the information required from their family and friends, then bring the sheet back to school so that the information can be used as part of a lesson.

Back at school
Make a large pictogram of favourite fruits. Ask the children to place a brick on the pictogram for each family member's choice of fruit. Discuss which is the most/least popular.

p61 COMPARING   MATHS TO SHARE

Learning outcomes
- Understand and use the vocabulary related to length.
- **Compare two lengths by direct comparison;** extend to more than two.

Lesson context
Provide practical activities in which children can compare items for length. Encourage the children to make estimates before they measure.

Setting the homework
Explain the activity to the children. Suggest that they look around the house for items with which they can compare their own height.

Back at school
Ask individual children to give examples of items that are taller than themselves and items that are shorter. Ask: *What was about the same height as you?*

p63 ODDS AND EVENS MATHS TO SHARE

Learning outcome
- Describe and extend number sequences: count on in twos from zero, then one, and begin to recognise odd or even numbers to about 20 as 'every other number'.

Lesson context
Ask the children to count in twos. With the children, say whether numbers are odd or even. The children can use interlocking cubes and count in twos and compare to find whether a number is odd or even.

Setting the homework
Explain that the activity is a game which can be played by one, two or more family members.

Back at school
Say some numbers, from zero to 20 and for each number, ask the children: *Is this odd or even?*

p64 DECADE NUMBER SEARCH MATHS TO SHARE

Learning outcomes
- Describe and extend number sequences: **count on and back in tens from and back to zero.**
  Count on in twos from zero, then one, and begin to recognise odd or even numbers to about 20 as 'every other number'.

Lesson context
Count together and around the class in patterns of twos and tens. Provide 100 square so that the children can follow the patterns of tens along it. Encourage them to say the decade numbers before and after given decades.

Setting the homework
Suggest places where the children could look around their homes to find 'tens' numbers, such as in books or on the clock. Ask them to bring the sheet back to school.

Back at school
Make a list on the flip chart of where the tens numbers were found and what the numbers were. Ask the children to read each number, then count on and back from it in tens.

p65 GRID COVER MATHS TO SHARE

Learning outcome
- Begin to know what each digit in a two-digit number represents. Partition a 'teens' number and begin to partition larger two-digit numbers into a multiple of 10 and ones (TU).

Lesson context
Help the children to recognise what each digit in a two-digit number represents and to partition a 'teens' number into tens and units by using place value arrow cards or a paper abacus and counters.

Setting the homework
Explain to the children how to spin the paper clip on each spinner on the sheet in order to make their 'teens' (TU) number.

Back at school
Write some 'teens' numbers on the flip chart and ask the children to say the number, and then to say it as a tens and units number. For example, for 14, say: *One ten and four units.*

p62 HOW TALL IS A CHAIR? GAMES AND PUZZLES

Learning outcomes
- Solve a given problem by sorting, classifying and organizing information in simple ways, such as in a list or simple table. Discuss and explain results.
- Understand and use the vocabulary related to length.
- **Suggest suitable standard or uniform non-standard units and measuring equipment to estimate, then measure, a length,** recording estimates and measurements as 'about...'.

Lesson context
Provide practical activities in which the children can estimate, then measure, using non-standard or standard units. Encourage them to respond to questions about, 'how long...?' by saying 'about', 'nearly' or 'just over', so that they show they understand that their measuring is approximate.

Setting the homework
Explain the activity. Suggest that they could use non-standard units, such as books or bricks to measure the chairs. Stress that all the items they use must be the same size, whatever that is: two paperback novels and an annual will not do!

Back at school
Discuss the units that the children chose for measuring. Ask: *How big was the count? Was this a good unit to use? Why? What might have been better? Why do you think that?*

p66 10 MORE, 10 LESS

Learning outcome
- **Within the range 0 to 30, say the number that is 1 or 10 more or less than any given number.**

Lesson context
Together and around the class say numbers that are 1 or 10 more or less than the starting number: *What is 1 more/less than 5, 8, 15...? What is 10 more/less than 20, 15, 13...?*

Setting the homework
Explain the activity to the children. Ask them to bring the sheet back to school when they have finished.

Back at school
Mark the work. Check that the children have understood what is meant by 10 more/less than a number. In a short mental activity session, check that all the children can say the number that is 1 or 10 more or less than a given number.

p67 COUNTER TOSS

Learning outcomes
- **Understand the operation of subtraction (as 'difference') and use the related vocabulary.**
- Begin to use the – and = signs to record mental calculations in a number sentence.

Lesson context
Ask the children to find the difference between two numbers. Provide examples using practical apparatus to model the concept of difference. Show two towers of interlocking cubes, one with five red cubes and the other with seven blue cubes. Discuss how there are two fewer red cubes than blue, or two more blue cubes than red. Explain that the difference between 5 and 7 (or 7 and 5) is 2.

Setting the homework
Explain the activity to the children. Ask them to bring the sheet back to school when they have finished.

Back at school
Review the subtractions together as part of a mental maths activity. Using an A3 enlargement of the homework sheet, point to a pair of numbers and ask a child to write the subtraction on the flip chart. Repeat for other examples.

p68 DIFFERENCE OF 6

Learning outcomes
- **Understand the operation of subtraction (as 'difference') and use the related vocabulary.**
- Begin to use the – and = signs to record mental calculations in a number sentence.

Lesson context
Ask the children to find the difference between two numbers. Provide examples using practical apparatus to model the concept of difference, for example two towers of interlocking cubes with a difference between the numbers of cubes of 2.

Setting the homework
Explain the activity to the children. Ask them to bring the sheet back to school with them when they have finished.

Back at school
Mark the homework, and check that there is a difference of 6 for each example. Provide other examples of finding differences during an oral maths session: find pairs of numbers with a difference of 4 or 5.

p69 PRICES

Learning outcomes
- Recognise coins of different values.
- Work out how to pay an exact sum using smaller coins.

Lesson context
Encourage the children to use coins with values greater than 1p, so that they are using combinations of coins to make an exact amount. Provide opportunities, such as a class shop, for the children to practise giving and receiving different amounts of money.

Setting the homework
Explain the activity. Suggest that the children use coins to help them find the exact amounts.

Back at school
Using an A3 enlargement of the homework sheet during an opening mental maths session. Ask individual children to find coins to pay for specific items on the sheet. Challenge the other children by asking: *Is this the only way? How else could we pay? Which way uses the least number of coins?*

p70 SHOPPING

Learning outcomes
- **Understand the operation of subtraction** as 'how many more to make' **and use the related vocabulary.**
- Recognise coins of different values. Find totals and change for values up to 10p.

Lesson context
Discuss ways of giving change from 10p, using 1p, 2p and 5p coins. Provide opportunities for children to practise giving change in realistic situations, such as a class shop. Encourage the children to count on from the cost of the item up to 10p.

Setting the homework
Explain the activity. Suggest to the children that they ask their helper to be the shopkeeper and that they act as the shopper.

Back at school
Use the activity on the sheet as part of an oral and mental starter activity. Provide the children with pots of coins, tell them how much the item costs and ask them to count out the change. Encourage them to use the least number of coins to give change.

p71 8p

Learning outcomes
- **Understand the operation of subtraction** as 'how many more to make' **and use the related vocabulary.**
- Recognise coins of different values. Work out how to pay an exact sum using smaller coins.

Lesson context
Provide experience of shopping activities using coins so children experience giving and receiving change, and paying an exact amount using small coins. You may decide to set up a class shop so that the children can role play being the customer and the shopkeeper.

Setting the homework
Explain the activity to the children. Ask them to bring the sheet back to school when they have finished.

Back at school
Mark the children's work. On the flip chart, record children's suggestions for paying 8p by writing addition sums, such as: 5p + 2p + 1p = 8p.

p72 TOTALS 10   GAMES AND PUZZLES

Learning outcomes
- **Understand the operation of subtraction** as 'how many more to make' **and use the related vocabulary.**
- Begin to recognise that more than two numbers can be added together.

Lesson context
Explain how to use complementary addition (or counting on) to work out what must be added to a number to make another number. Encourage the children to count on from one number to the next to find the difference. Say a number which is the total and ask the children to find three or more numbers to add to make that total. Encourage them to count on from one number to the next to solve the problem.

Setting the homework
Explain the activity. Ask the children to bring the sheet back to school when they have finished.

Back at school
Mark the work. Discuss their work with any children who found this difficult in order to identify the difficulty and provide further examples.

p73 STAMPS   GAMES AND PUZZLES

Learning outcomes
- **Use mental strategies to solve simple problems** set in money contexts, **using counting, addition, subtraction, doubling and halving, explaining methods and reasoning orally.**
- Choose and use appropriate number operations and mental strategies to solve problems.

Lesson context
Encourage the children to use their mental calculation strategies to solve word problems within money contexts. For more complex problems, it may help to write some information on the flip chart and ask the children to use paper and pencil to record their working. Ask: *How did you work it out? Is there another way?*

Setting the homework
Explain the activity to the children. Suggest that the children cut out some 'stamps' and use these to help them to solve the problems.

Back at school
Review the homework. Ask for suggestions for each price, from 1p to 20p. Discuss how for some prices there will be different answers possible.

p74 FOOD COMPARISON   MATHS TO SHARE

Learning outcome
- **Compare two masses by direct comparison;** extend to more than two.

Lesson context
Provide a range of different-shaped and sized parcels for comparing weights by holding the parcels. Check that the children are comparing weight, not volume. Sometimes the visual size of the parcel is seen by children as taking precedence over what they can feel: it's bigger, therefore, it must be heavier.

Setting the homework
Explain the activity to the children. Discuss the range of things from home which they might use, such as cans, packets and items of fruit or vegetables.

Back at school
Provide some items for comparison of weight. Ask the children to work in groups to order the items from lightest to heaviest. Provide a short space of time for the children to check the ordering of items for other groups.

p75 WEIGHING   MATHS TO SHARE

Learning outcome
- **Suggest suitable standard or uniform non-standard units and measuring equipment to estimate, then measure, a mass.**

Lesson context
Provide a range of different weight parcels for estimating and weighing, a range of weighing machines such as a bucket balance, pan and weights scale, and uniform non-standard units such as cubes, plastic masses or marbles. Check that the children estimate with their chosen unit, then measure. Discuss why they chose the unit and if it was appropriate, taking into account the nature of the count.

Setting the homework
Explain the activity to the children. Ask the children to bring the sheet back to school when they have completed it.

Back at school
Using an A3 enlargement of the homework sheet, ask the children to suggest which items should be joined together. Discuss their choices and encourage them to suggest other items which could be weighed with each scale and say why this would be suitable. Some scales can be joined with more than one item to be weighed, for example the flour and the margarine would be measured on the kitchen scales.

p76 ABOUT THE SAME

MATHS TO SHARE

Learning outcome
• **Use mental strategies to solve simple problems** set in measurement contexts, **using counting, addition, subtraction, doubling and halving, explaining methods and reasoning orally.**

Lesson context
Encourage the children to use their developing skills of estimation before they weigh the objects. They should then measure the weight before comparing their estimate and measurement. Set some problems which involve calculations so that they consider which mental strategies to use to solve the problems, such as: *How many scoops of sand are needed to balance five marbles? How many do you think you will need to balance ten marbles?*

Setting the homework
Ask the children to use their reading book to make their comparisons of weight.

Back at school
Discuss the range of items that the children found. Ask the children to decide which of several items in the classroom would weigh about the same as a reading book, then check using a balance.

p77 SHAPE PATTERN

MATHS TO SHARE

Learning outcomes
• **Use everyday language to describe features of familiar 2-D shapes,** including the circle, triangle, square, rectangle... referring to properties such as the shapes of flat faces, or the number of faces or corners... or the number and types of sides.
• Make and describe models, patterns and pictures using construction kits, everyday materials, Plasticine...

Lesson context
Provide shape tiles, gummed paper shapes and so on, for the children to use to make pictures and patterns. Encourage the children to discuss the properties of the shapes they use, such as: *It has a curved side. It has four straight sides....*

Setting the homework
Explain to the children that they will need to cut out the shape tiles on the sheet. When they have finished their pattern they can colour it in if they wish.

Back at school
Make a display of the returned patterns, perhaps in 'Our Pattern Book'. Encourage the children to compare the different patterns that were made and to discuss the properties of the shapes.

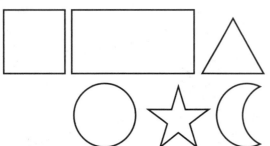

p78 HALF A SHAPE

MATHS TO SHARE

Learning outcome
• Fold shapes in half and then make them into symmetrical patterns.

Lesson context
Ask the children to make symmetrical shapes by folding and cutting. Demonstrate by folding a sheet of paper in half, drawing half a butterfly on one side of the folded piece of paper then cutting it out. Open up the shape and discuss with the children what they see. Point out how one half is a 'reflection' of the other. Provide opportunities for the children to make symmetrical patterns and shapes, such as making ink blot paintings.

Setting the homework
Explain the activity. Encourage the children to cut out the shapes carefully, colour them in and bring them back to school so that they can be displayed in 'Our Pattern Book'.

Back at school
Mount the shapes into a class pattern book. Encourage the children to look at the shapes and discuss in what ways the two sides of each are the same and in what ways they are different.

p79 JIGSAW

GAMES AND PUZZLES

Learning outcomes
• Solve simple mathematical problems or puzzles; recognise and predict from simple patterns and relationships. Suggest extensions by asking 'What if...?' or 'what could I try next?'

Lesson context
Provide shape tiles so that the children can make pictures and patterns in order to solve some shape problems. Set a problem such as: *Which shape tiles would you choose to make a picture of a car? What else could you use?*

Setting the homework
Explain that the picture on the sheet is a jigsaw to be cut out and coloured. The children can colour in the picture before they cut up the pieces if they prefer.

Back at school
Provide some old greetings cards which the children can cut up to make jigsaws. Say: *Use just three cuts to cut up this picture. Can your partner put it together? Now use four/five... cuts for this picture.*

p80 ODD OR EVEN SNAP

MATHS TO SHARE

Learning outcome
• Describe and extend number sequences: count on in twos from zero, then one, and begin to recognise odd or even numbers to about 20 as 'every other number'.

Lesson context
Say the counting patterns for ones, twos and tens together and around the class. Encourage the children to say the number patterns, counting rhythmically and at a good pace. Check that children can distinguish odd numbers from even numbers, and recognise that an odd number ends with a 1, 3, 5, 7 or 9 and an even number with 0, 2, 4, 6 or 8.

Setting the homework
Explain the activity to the children. Decide whether to provide a set of numeral cards for any children who do not think they have playing cards at home.

Back at school
Reinforce the concept of odd and even numbers by asking children to hold up their hand if the numeral card that you show has an odd number. Repeat for even numbers.

p81 COUNTING PICTURES

MATHS TO SHARE

Learning outcome
- **Count reliably at least 20 objects.**

Lesson context
Ask the children to count at least 20 objects accurately. Check that the children have efficient counting strategies and that each item is counted just once.

Setting the homework
Explain the activity. Ask the children to bring the sheet back to school when they have completed it.

Back at school
Mark the children's work. Check the counting skills of any children with mistakes and encourage them to touch and count, remembering which items they have already been counted and which have still to be counted.

p82 ADDING

GAMES AND PUZZLES

Learning outcome
- Investigate a general statement about familiar numbers by finding examples that satisfy it.

Lesson context
Provide challenges such as: *There are many different ways to make a total of 10. Find five different ways.* Write the different solutions that the children suggest on the flip chart and encourage them to see that the original statement is true.

Setting the homework
Explain the task. Ask the children to bring the sheet back to school when they have completed the work.

Back at school
Mark the work. Check that the children have understood the general statement that order is not important to the answer when adding up and have provided sums to show it is true.

p83 SPORTS DAY

MATHS TO SHARE

Learning outcomes
- **Read and write numerals from 0 to at least 20.**
- **Understand and use the vocabulary of comparing and ordering numbers,** including ordinal numbers to at least 20.

Lesson context
Ask the children to order numbers to at least 20. Use ordinal language to explain the position of children in a line, or numeral cards on a washing line. Encourage the children to respond to questions about order using ordinal language. For example: *Who is fifth in the line? What position is Jack?*

Setting the homework
Explain the activity to the children.

Back at school
Using an A3 enlargement of the homework sheet, ask the children to describe the positions of the children in the race using ordinal language. Ask, for example: *Who is first? Which child is last? Where is Subhia?*

p84 COMPARING AND ORDERING NUMBERS

GAMES AND PUZZLES

Learning outcomes
- **Understand and use the vocabulary of comparing and ordering numbers,** including ordinal numbers to at least 20.
- Compare two familiar numbers, say which is more or less, and give a number which lies between them.

Lesson context
Say two numbers out loud and ask the children: *Which is the higher and which is the lower?* Then ask them which number lies between those two numbers. Provide examples where there are several possible answers, such as *...a number between 2 and 12,* and encourage the children to find all the whole number answers.

Setting the homework
Explain the activity to the children. Ask them to bring the sheet back to school when it is completed.

Back at school
Mark the children's work. Check with any children who have errors in their work that they understand what is meant by 'more', 'less' and 'between'.

p85 ADDITION PATTERNS FOR 13

MATHS TO SHARE

Learning outcomes
- Use known number facts and place value to add or subtract a pair of numbers mentally within the range 0 to at least 10, then 0 to at least 20.
- Use patterns of similar calculations.

Lesson context
Write addition patterns such as $0 + 5 = 5$; $1 + 4 = 5$; $2 + 3 = 5$... on to the flip chart. Encourage the children to complete the addition patterns, then provide further examples for them to complete for themselves.

Setting the homework
Explain the activity to the children. Ask them to write their addition sums in order. When they have finished they should bring the sheet back to school.

Back at school
Mark the work. Talk to any children who made errors to check whether they misunderstood or simply made a small mistake.

 **ADDITION GRID**   **p86**

MATHS TO SHARE

Learning outcome
• Put the larger number first and count on in ones, including beyond 10.

Lesson context
Explain and practise the addition strategy of putting the larger number first and counting on in ones. Provide examples which include totals beyond 10, such as 7 + 5. Record addition sums on the flip chart using symbols. Extend this to adding a single digit to a 'teens' number, without crossing the ten, such as 11 + 3 = 14.

Setting the homework
Explain the activity. Ask the children to bring back their sheets when these are completed.

Back at school
Mark the work. Talk to any child who made errors to determine whether there is a misunderstanding or whether the child simply made a small mistake.

 **p87** **TRIO CARDS**

MATHS TO SHARE

Learning outcomes
• **Understand the operation of addition, and of subtraction (as 'take away' and 'difference') and use the related vocabulary.**
• Begin to understand that addition can be done in any order.

Lesson context
Write three related numbers on the flip chart such as 5, 7 and 12. Ask the children to find four related facts using these numbers: 5 + 7 = 12; 7 + 5 = 12; 12 – 7 = 5; and 12 – 5 = 7. Explain that if one fact is known then the others can be worked out. Provide further examples for the children to try. Discuss the fact that addition can be done in any order.

Setting the homework
Explain the activity to the children. Remind them that if they do not know a fact that they should use their mental strategies to work it out.

Back at school
Use the trio cards idea as part of an oral starter activity. Make enlarged versions for whole class use.

p88 **THREE NUMBER ADDITION**

MATHS TO SHARE

Learning outcomes
• **Understand the operation of addition and use the related vocabulary.**
• Begin to understand that addition can be done in any order.
• Begin to recognise that more than two numbers can be added together.

Lesson context
Encourage the children to use their mental calculation strategies, such as putting the larger number first, to combine three numbers. Provide examples using numbers less than 10, such as 6 + 3 + 4.

Setting the homework
Explain the activity to the children. Ask them to bring their sheet back to school when it is completed.

Back at school
Mark the homework. Where a child has an error, discuss the work and decide whether this is due to a misconception or simply an error in calculation.

 **FAVOURITE OUTINGS**   **p89**

MATHS TO SHARE

Learning outcomes
• Solve a given problem by sorting, classifying and organising information in simple ways, such as: using objects or pictures.
  Discuss and explain results.

Lesson context
Explain that the children will be solving problems about themselves and recording their results in a simple graph made with towers of cubes, or gummed paper shapes. Use one cube/shape per positive response. Use examples such as: *What is your favourite flavour of crisps?* Ask questions when the graph is completed such as: *Which is more/less popular than...? How do we know that? Which is the most popular flavour?*

Setting the homework
Explain the activity to the children and ask them to bring their completed sheet back to school so that a large, class graph can be made.

Back at school
Make a large, class graph and ask the children to add their data by using gummed paper squares in the appropriate columns for the outings. The numbers for each outing may be large, so help the children with the counting. Ask: *Which is the most/least popular?*

p90 **MARBLE GRAB**

MATHS TO SHARE

Learning outcomes
• Solve a given problem by sorting, classifying and organising information in simple ways, such as: in a list.
  Discuss and explain results.

Lesson context
Provide opportunities for the children to make lists, such as: *Write down all the even numbers between 1 and 10.* Ask the children to work in groups, with a helper to scribe as necessary, to collect some data. Put it into a list. They could answer a question such as: *What pets do you have at home?* Transfer the data on to a class chart using one square to represent each pet. Ask questions such as: *Which are more popular: cats or dogs? How do we know? How many more cats are there than dogs?*

Setting the homework
Explain that this is an activity in which everyone at home can join in, but that the child should count the marbles (or other items) and record the results.

Back at school
Look at the sheets, and choose one with a good range of data. If possible, let the child put their data on to a larger version of the recording chart drawn on to the flip chart. Looking at the data together, ask questions of all the children, such as: *Who held the most/least? Who held four more than... ? How many fewer did... hold than... ?*

p91 TIME SHEET · MATHS TO SHARE

Learning outcomes
- Understand and use the vocabulary related to time.
- Read the time to the hour or half hour on analogue clocks

Lesson context
Give each child a cardboard clock with moveable hands. Ask the children to set the hands of their clocks to 'o'clock' and 'half-past' times that you say. When they are confident with this, ask them questions such as: *Show me two hours before 5 o'clock; three hours after 6 o'clock....* Discuss what the children do at different times of the day, such as 12 o'clock (lunch time) and what time it is when they get up or go to bed.

Setting the homework
Explain the activity to the children. Read the times on the clocks on the sheet together. Ask the children to bring their sheets back to school when these are completed.

Back at school
Discuss the task with any child who has found it difficult, to ascertain whether they have misunderstood and need further help. You could bind the homework sheets together to make a 'Time Book'.

p92 DAYS OF THE WEEK · MATHS TO SHARE

Learning outcomes
- Understand and use the vocabulary related to time.
- Order familiar events in time.
- Know the days of the week and the seasons of the year.

Lesson context
Show the children some pictures that represent the seasons and discuss the features of each season. Say the days of the week in order, and ask questions such as: *What day is it today? What day was it yesterday? What day will it be tomorrow?*

Setting the homework
Explain the activity. Ask the children to bring the sheet back to school when it is completed.

Back at school
Mark the children's work. Ask the class questions such as: *If today is Monday, what day will tomorrow be? What day was yesterday? What day will it be in two days time?...*

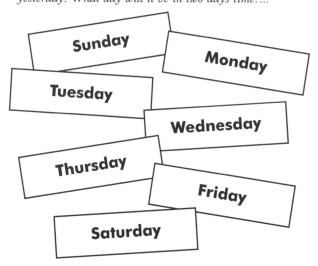

p93 HAND SPAN MEASURE · GAMES AND PUZZLES

Learning outcome
- **Use mental strategies to solve problems** set in measurement contexts, **using counting, addition, subtraction, doubling and halving, explaining methods and reasoning orally.**

Lesson context
Set some length problems for the children to solve, such as: *Estimate, then check using non-standard units, how far up the wall you can reach.* Ask the children to explain which units they chose and to justify the choice. Encourage them to record their estimates and measures as 'about ...'. Include some word problems such as: *My pencil is 6 cubes long. John's pencil is as long as 8 cubes. Which one is longer? How much longer?*

Setting the homework
Discuss making estimates and checking by measuring. Explain what is meant by a 'hand span'. Ask the children to bring their sheet back to school with them when it is complete.

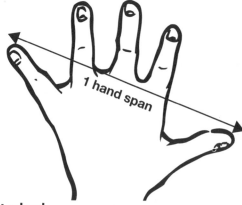

1 hand span

Back at school
Ask individual children to give examples of what they measured and how long the items were. Discuss why it is that other children may have measured the same sort of things, but had different answers (their hands are a different size; the items to be measured were of a different size).

p94 ABOUT A KILOGRAM · GAMES AND PUZZLES

Learning outcome
- **Use mental strategies to solve problems** set in measurement contexts, **using counting, addition, subtraction, doubling and halving, explaining methods and reasoning orally.**

Lesson context
Set some weight problems for the children to solve, such as: *Estimate, then check using non-standard units, how much your shoe weighs.* Ask the children to explain which units they chose and to justify the choice. Encourage them to record their estimates and measures as 'about ...'. Include some word problems such as: *Five bricks balance an apple. Six bricks balance a pear. The apple and pear are put on the scales together. How many bricks will balance them?*

Setting the homework
Discuss making comparisons of weight by using your hands. Ask the children to bring the sheet back to school when it is completed.

Back at school
Show the children a 1kg mass and ask individuals to find things in the classroom which weigh 'about a kilogram'. Ask the children for suggestions for things that they could find at home which weigh about a kilogram. You could make 'A Kilogram Book' from the homework sheets.

TERM 3

p95 COUNTING MANY SHAPES
MATHS TO SHARE

Learning outcome
• **Count reliably at least 20 objects.**

Lesson context
Provide opportunities for counting between 10 and 20 objects set out as straight lines, arrays, circles and randomly. Encourage the children to point and count, rather than touch and count, and to remember which items they have counted and which remain to be counted.

Setting the homework
Explain that the items on the sheet should be counted by pointing rather than touching. Ask the children to bring the sheet back to school when it is completed.

Back at school
Mark the work. Discuss their work with children who have errors and decide whether they need further experience of counting.

p96 WHAT COMES NEXT?
GAMES AND PUZZLES

Learning outcomes
• Describe and extend number sequences: **count on and back in ones from any small number, and in tens from and back to zero;** count on in twos from zero, then one, and begin to recognise odd or even numbers to about 20 as 'every other number'; count in steps of 5 from zero to 20 or more, then back again; begin to count on in steps of 3 from zero.

Lesson context
Count together and round the class in twos, fives and threes. Challenge the children to say whether specific numbers are odd or even. Provide opportunities for continuing counting patterns, starting on any small number.

Setting the homework
Explain the activity to the children and ask them to bring the sheet back to school when it is completed.

Back at school
Using an A3 enlargement of the homework sheet, review the homework together during an oral maths session. Decide whether the children can check their own work. Discuss each pattern and encourage the children to continue it by chanting beyond what is on the sheet.

p97 MISSING NUMBERS
GAMES AND PUZZLES

Learning outcome
• **Understand and use the language of comparing and ordering numbers,** including ordinal numbers to at least 20. Compare two familiar numbers, say which is more or less, and give a number which lies between them.

Lesson context
Ask the children to say a number which comes between two given numbers. Then ask them to put short sequences of numbers into numerical order.

Setting the homework
Explain the activity to the children. Ask them to bring their completed sheets back to school.

Back at school
Mark the homework. Discuss the work with any child who had errors and decide whether they need further help.

p98 COUNTER MOVES
GAMES AND PUZZLES

Learning outcome
• **Order numbers to at least 20,** and position them on a number track.

Lesson context
Line up ten children and count them with the class. Ask: *Who is first/last/second...?* Ask children to change places with those who are lined up: *Jeni stand between Sajid and Raza. What number are you?*

Setting the homework
Explain that when playing the game each counter is moved in turn, so that after the first roll of the dice the first counter moves, after the second roll the second counter moves and so on.

Back at school
Play the game as part of an oral and mental starter. Use an A3 enlargement of the sheet and attach the counters with Blu-Tack. After each move of the counter, ask: *Who is winning? Who is second...?*

p99 CARD ADD
MATHS TO SHARE

Learning outcomes
• **Understand the operation of addition, and use the related vocabulary.**
• Begin to recognise that more than two numbers can be added together.
• Use known number facts and place value to add a pair of numbers mentally within the range 0 to at least 10, then 0 to at least 20.

Lesson context
Write the numbers 1, 2, 3 and 4 on the flip chart and ask the children to choose three of these numbers for an addition sum. Write the sum and the total and ask the children to explain their addition strategies. Ask the children to draw three numeral cards from a pack of cards. Each time they should write the addition sum and total for these cards.

Setting the homework
Explain the activity to the children. Decide whether to loan some sets of numeral cards to children who do not have playing cards at home.

Back at school
During an oral starter, ask the children to suggest sums to be written on to an A3 enlargement of the homework sheet. Discuss the addition strategies the children used and ask: *Is there another way of working this out?*

p100 BRIDGING 10
MATHS TO SHARE

Learning outcomes
• **Understand the operation of addition, and use the related vocabulary.**
• Begin to bridge through 10, and later 20, when adding a single-digit number.

Lesson context
Write an addition sum on the flip chart where the answer is greater than 10, such as $6 + 8$. Explain that this can be worked out in two mental steps: $6 + 4 + 4 = 10 + 4 = 14$. Provide further examples until the children are confident with this strategy.

Setting the homework
Explain the activity to the children. Ask the children to bring the completed sheet back to school.

Back at school
Mark the homework. Discuss their work with any child who had errors and decide whether they need further practice.

$$\triangle \quad + \quad 6 \quad = \quad 15$$

$$9 \quad + \quad \square \quad = \quad 15$$

p101 CHANGE FROM 20p

MATHS TO SHARE

Learning outcomes
- **Understand the operation of addition, and use the related vocabulary.**
- Begin to bridge through 10, and later 20, when adding a single-digit number.
- Recognise coins of different values. Find totals and change from up to 20p. Work out how to pay an exact sum using smaller coins.

Lesson context
Using money contexts, ask the children to total two amounts so that they bridge 10. For example, for adding 7p and 5p: 7p + 5p = 7p + 3p + 2p = 10p + 2p = 12p. Ask the children to calculate the change from 20p. Provide further examples of bridging 10 and finding the change from 20p.

Setting the homework
Explain the activity to the children. Ask them to bring the completed sheet back to school.

Back at school
Mark the homework. Discuss any errors with individual children and decide whether they need further help.

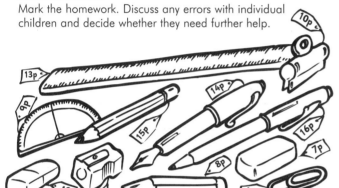

p102 TOTAL 14

GAMES AND PUZZLES

Learning outcomes
- **Understand the operation of addition, and use the related vocabulary.**
- Begin to bridge through 10, and later 20, when adding a single-digit number.

Lesson context
Write the numerals 1 to 20 on the flip chart and ask: *Which two numbers will total 13?* Challenge the children to find as many pairs as they can which total 13. Ask: *How did you work it out?* Encourage the use of the bridging 10 strategy. Repeat for other totals.

Setting the homework
Explain the activity. Ask the children to use the bridging 10 strategy to help them to find their answers. Ask them to bring the completed sheets back to school.

Back at school
Write the numbers 0 to 14 on the flip chart and challenge the children to find as many pairs as they can which total 14. For each one, ask: *How did you work that out?* Encourage the use of the bridging 10 strategy. Decide whether the children should mark their own homework during this session.

p103 ADDITION SUMS

GAMES AND PUZZLES

Learning outcomes
- **Understand the operation of addition, and use the related vocabulary.**
- Begin to bridge through 10, and later 20, when adding a single-digit number.

Lesson context
Ask the children to work out a sum such as 8 + □ = 12. Now write 4 + □ = 12. Encourage the use of the bridging 10 strategy. Encourage the children to explain what they notice: that the same three numbers are used, so that if you know the answer to one sum you can derive the other. Ask the children to write sums in the format □ + △ = ○ where the answer is between 10 and 15.

Setting the homework
Explain the activity to the children. Ask them to bring their sheet back to school with them when it is completed.

Back at school
Using an A3 enlargement of the homework sheet, ask for some answers to the sums. Challenge the children to work out the answers mentally and to explain their strategies. Encourage the use of the bridging 10 strategy.

p104 SUBTRACTION SUMS

GAMES AND PUZZLES

Learning outcomes
- **Understand the operation of subtraction (as 'take away'), and use the related vocabulary.**
- Begin to use the – and = signs to record mental calculations in a number sentence, and to recognise and use symbols such as □ or △ to stand for an unknown number.
- Use known number facts and place value to add or subtract a pair of numbers mentally within the range 0 to at least 10, then 0 to at least 20.

Lesson context
Write on the flip chart 15 – 3 = □ and ask the children to solve this using a number line. Now write 15 – □ = 12 and ask for the answer; then □ – 3 = 12. Ask what they notice about the three number sentences. Provide further examples of linked subtraction facts for the children to solve.

Setting the homework
Explain the activity to the children and suggest that if they find this difficult they should draw themselves a number line. Ask them to bring the sheets back to school when these are completed.

Back at school
Mark the homework. Discuss their work with any child who has errors and decide whether they would benefit from further experience of subtraction.

$$16 \quad - \quad \triangle \quad = \quad \square$$

p105 TOTAL 20p   GAMES AND PUZZLES

Learning outcome
- **Use mental strategies to solve simple problems** set in money contexts, **using counting, addition, subtraction, doubling and halving, explaining methods and reasoning orally.**

Lesson context
Provide some problems to be solved set in 'real life' or money contexts, such as: *I am thinking of two numbers which total 10. What might these numbers be?* or: *Tara had 20p. She spent 8p. How much does she have left?* Encourage the children to record their answers and to explain how they worked these out.

Setting the homework
Explain the activity. Suggest to the children that they would find it useful to use some coins to help them find the solutions to this.

Back at school
Ask the children to suggest some solutions and to count out these coins to show that they total 20p. Ask: *Which way uses the least number of coins?*

p106 WATER FUN   MATHS TO SHARE

Learning outcomes
- Understand and use the vocabulary related to capacity. Measure using uniform non-standard units or standard units.
- **Suggest suitable standard or uniform non-standard units and measuring equipment to estimate, then measure, a capacity,** recording estimates and measurements as 'about three beakers full'.

Lesson context
Provide opportunities for estimating and measuring the capacity of different containers using uniform non-standard units such as yogurt pots, spoons, cups. Encourage the children to estimate first and then to compare their estimate with their measurement. Ask them to record their measurement as 'about…' so that they begin to understand that measuring may be approximate.

Setting the homework
Explain the activity to the children. Talk about how this activity could make a mess and how this could be avoided by taking care, and by wiping up any spills.

Back at school
Discuss the activity during an oral maths session. Talk about how this sort of measuring is approximate.

p107 CAPACITY COMPARISON   MATHS TO SHARE

Learning outcome
- **Use mental strategies to solve simple problems** set in measurement contexts, **using counting, addition, subtraction, doubling and halving, explaining methods and reasoning orally.**

Lesson context
Provide some word problems set in capacity contexts, such as: *A full jug holds six cupfuls. How many cupfuls do two full jugs hold?* Ask the children to explain how they worked it out, and write the answer as a number sentence. Repeat for other problems.

Setting the homework
Explain the activity to the children. Ask them to bring the sheets back to school when these are completed.

Back at school
Mark the homework. For any child with errors, decide if they need further help.

p108 PICTURE THESE   MATHS TO SHARE

Learning outcomes
- Use everyday language to describe position, direction and movement.
- Talk about things that turn. Make whole turns and half turns.

Lesson context
Talk about things in the classroom which will turn about a point, such as door handles and clock hands. Then discuss things that turn about a line such as doors and book pages. Set some challenges for the children to solve, such as programming a Roamer to move from the book case to the carpet; sorting 3-D shapes by their properties; finding objects in the classroom that will roll, slide, or roll and slide.

Setting the homework
Explain the activity to the children. Suggest that they look at home for the things that are pictured.

Back at school
During an oral session discuss with the children what objects they found for each category and why the objects fitted the category.

p109 COLOUR PATTERN   MATHS TO SHARE

Learning outcome
- Use one or more shapes to make, describe and continue repeating patterns…

Lesson context
Begin a repeating pattern with two shapes and ask the children to continue it. When they are confident with this, extend this to copying and continuing patterns with three different shapes. Ask the children to make their own repeating patterns using three different shapes.

Setting the homework
Explain the activity to the children. Ask them to bring the patterns back to school when they are completed.

Back at school
During an oral session, show some of the patterns to the children. Ask them to 'say' the pattern and to continue it. Decide whether to make an 'Our Pattern Book' to display the patterns.

 p110 FIND THE WAY HOME   GAMES AND PUZZLES

Learning outcome
- Solve simple mathematical problems or puzzles; recognise and predict from simple patterns and relationships. Suggest extensions by asking 'What if...?' or 'What could I try next?' Explain methods and reasoning orally.

Lesson context
Provide some shape problems for the children to solve, such as a simple two-piece tangram cut from a square, and ask the children to move the pieces to make new, given shapes.

Setting the homework
Explain that this puzzle is about finding different ways home. Discuss how the children go home from school: do they always go the same way? Who has different routes?

Back at school
Using an A3 enlargement of the sheet, ask the children to suggest different routes home. Mark these onto the sheet. Talk about the direction of movement, using words such as: *turn left, turn right, go straight on.*

 p111 NUMBER PATTERN BOARD GAME   GAMES AND PUZZLES

Learning outcome
- Describe and extend number sequences: count in twos from zero, then one, and begin to recognize odd or even numbers to about 20 as 'every other number'; count in steps of 5 from zero to 20 or more, then back again; begin to count on in steps of 3 from zero.

Lesson context
Count in 2s, 3s and 5s together and around the class. Ask: *Is this an odd/even number?* Write some number patterns on the flip chart for 2s, 3s and 5s and ask the children to continue them.

Setting the homework
Explain the activity to the children. Play the game through before they take it home so that they are clear how it is played.

Back at school
Play the game again during an oral session. Encourage the children to count at a good pace in 2s, 3s or 5s, as needed.

 p112 NUMBER PATTERNS   GAMES AND PUZZLES

Learning outcome
- Describe and extend number sequences: **count on and back in ones from any small number, and in tens from and back to zero;** count in twos from zero, then one, and begin to recognize odd or even numbers to about 20 as 'every other number'; count in steps of five from zero to 20 or more, then back again; begin to count on in steps of three from zero.

Lesson context
Provide opportunities for the children to create their own number patterns, such as: *Write a number pattern which includes the number 4.* Other patterns could include those which have just odd/even numbers or a pattern with no 10.

Setting the homework
Explain the activity to the children. Ask them to bring their sheets back to school when these are completed.

Back at school
Write some of the patterns on to the flip chart and ask the children to describe each pattern. Decide whether to make an 'Our Pattern Book' to display the completed sheets.

p113 MAKING 19   GAMES AND PUZZLES

Learning outcomes
- Solve simple mathematical problems or puzzles; recognize and predict from simple patterns and relationships. Suggest extensions by asking 'What if...?' or 'what could I try next?'
- Investigate a general statement about familiar numbers by finding examples that satisfy it.
- Explain methods and reasoning orally.

Lesson context
Set some word problems for the children to solve, such as: *Write as many different ways as you can of making the number 20.* Include some investigations of general statements such as: *I can pay for anything from 1p to 5p if I have two 2p coins and one 1p coin.* Ask the children to record their ideas using number sentences and to explain their strategies.

Setting the homework
Explain the activity to the children. Ask them to bring the sheet back to school when it is completed.

Back at school
Mark the children's work. Decide whether any children with errors need further experience of this.

 p114 ORDERING TO 20   GAMES AND PUZZLES

Learning outcome
- **Understand and use the vocabulary of comparing and ordering numbers,** including ordinal numbers to at least 20.

Lesson context
Ask the children to show two-digit numbers using arrow cards and discuss for each number how many tens and how many units there are. When they are confident with this, ask them to record the numbers you say using a paper abacus and counters. Ask them to write some numbers that you say in order.

Setting the homework
Explain the activity to the children. Explain that the game can be played with one, two, three or four people. Decide whether to loan some numeral cards to any children who do not have playing cards at home.

Back at school
As part of an oral session, write some numbers, out of order, on the flip chart and ask the children to help to put them in order. Ask them to explain why each number belongs in its place.

p115 COUNTER COUNT   MATHS TO SHARE

Learning outcomes
- Understand and use the vocabulary of estimation.
- Give a sensible estimate of a number of objects than can be checked by counting (e.g. up to about 30 objects).

Lesson context
Provide opportunities for estimating numerical quantities, such as asking how may beads there are in a jar. Ask the children to check their estimate by counting.

Setting the homework
Explain the activity to the children. Explain that counters, small bricks or larger coins could be used. Ask the children to bring their sheet back to school when it is completed.

Back at school
Mark the homework. Where children have large differences between their estimates and counts decide whether they need further experience of estimating.

p116 WHERE DOES IT FIT?

MATHS TO SHARE

Learning outcomes
- **Within the range 0 to 30, say the number that is 1 or 10 more or less than any given number.**
- **Order numbers to at least 20,** and position them on a number track.

Lesson context
Ask questions about ordering of numbers such as: *What is one before 6, 13, 30... What is one after/less than/more than...?* Provide further opportunities for children to order numbers to at least 20, using numeral cards. The numbers are randomised and the children order them, explaining for each move why the card fits where they have placed it.

Setting the homework
Explain the activity to the children. Ask them to bring their sheets back to school when these are completed.

Back at school
Using an A3 enlargement of the sheet, ask the children to help you to fill in the missing numbers. For each response ask: *Why does that number belong there?*

p117 NUMBER COVER UP

GAMES AND PUZZLES

Learning outcomes
- **Understand the operation of addition, and of subtraction (as 'take away', 'difference',** and 'how many more to make') **and use the related vocabulary.**
- Use known number facts and place value to add or subtract a pair of numbers mentally within the range 0 to at least 10, then 0 to at least 20.

Lesson context
Provide opportunities for the children to work out linked additions and subtractions such as 5 + 4; 15 + 4; 15 – 4; 5 – 4. Encourage them children to explain their calculation strategies, and to use the facts that they know to work out the answers mentally.

Setting the homework
Explain the activity to the children, and point out that this is a good game to play with a friend or family member.

Back at school
Using an A3 enlargement of the homework sheet, play the game with the children. As they solve each problem ask: *How did you work it out?*

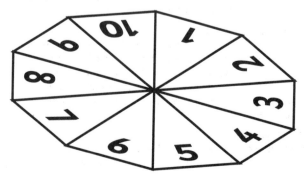

p118 BOX ADD

GAMES AND PUZZLES

Learning outcomes
- **Understand the operation of addition, and use the related vocabulary.**
- Begin to bridge through 10, and later 20, when adding a single-digit number.

Lesson context
Provide opportunities for the children to bridge through 10, and later through 20, as they add. Ask them to use two steps to cross the tens: 9 + 4 = 9 + 1 + 3 = 10 + 3 = 13; and 19 + 4 = 19 + 1 + 3 = 20 + 3 = 23. Provide further examples for the children to practise until they are confident with this strategy.

Setting the homework
Explain the activity to the children. Ask them to bring their sheets back to school when they have been completed.

Back at school
Mark the homework. Decide whether to provide further experience for children with errors.

p119 TOTALS

GAMES AND PUZZLES

Learning outcomes
- **Understand the operation of addition, and use the related vocabulary.**
- Use known number facts and place value to add a pair of numbers mentally within the range 0 to at least 10, then 0 to at least 20.

Lesson context
Ask the children to add two numbers which cross the 20 boundary and encourage them to explain their mental strategies. For example, for 18 + 5: 18 add 2 is 20 and 3 more is 23. Provide further opportunities for children to practise their strategies for crossing the 20 boundary when adding.

Setting the homework
Explain the activity to the children. Ask them to bring their sheets back to school when they have been completed.

Back at school
Mark the homework. Decide whether to provide further experience for children with errors.

p120 GIVING CHANGE

MATHS TO SHARE

Learning outcome
- Recognise coins of different values. Find totals and change from up to 20p. Work out how to pay an exact sum using smaller coins.

Lesson context
Provide some parcels with prices between 1p and 10p. Choose three of these and ask: *How much will these cost in total?* Encourage the children to work mentally to calculate the cost and then work out the change from 20p. They can use coins to model this. Ask the children to work in small groups, taking turns to act as the shopkeeper or a customer, buying three items and giving change from 20p.

Setting the homework
Explain the activity to the children. Suggest that they may find it helpful to use some money to count out the change.

Back at school
Make an A3 enlargement of the homework sheet. As part of an oral maths session, ask the children to take turns to be the shopkeeper and the customer. Encourage the shopkeeper to count out the change so that everyone can check it.

p121 TOTALLING 19 · GAMES AND PUZZLES

Learning outcomes
- **Use mental strategies to solve simple problems** set in 'real life' contexts, **using counting, addition, subtraction, doubling and halving, explaining methods and reasoning orally.**
- Choose and use appropriate number operations and mental strategies to solve problems.

Lesson context
Set some problems in 'real life' contexts, for the children to solve. Encourage them to write a number sentence to show their solution and to explain the mental strategies that they used. Include problems such as: *I am thinking of two numbers. When I add them the answer is 8. What could my two numbers be?*

Setting the homework
Explain the activity to the children. Ask them to bring their completed sheets back to school.

Back at school
Mark the homework. Decide whether to provide further experiences of solving word problems for those children who found this difficult.

p122 PAYING 18p · GAMES AND PUZZLES

Learning outcomes
- **Use mental strategies to solve simple problems** set in money contexts, **using counting, addition, subtraction, doubling and halving, explaining methods and reasoning orally.**
- Choose and use appropriate number operations and mental strategies to solve problems.

Lesson context
Set some word problems and ask the children to solve these using their mental strategies. They should then write a number sentence to show their thinking. Problems could include: *Which coins do you need to make 13p? Find two different ways.*

Setting the homework
Explain the activity to the children. Remind them that they will need some coins.

Back at school
Mark the homework. Decide whether to give further experience to any children who found this difficult.

p123 MEASURING CAPACITY · MATHS TO SHARE

Learning outcomes
- Understand and use the vocabulary related to capacity.
- **Suggest suitable standard or uniform non-standard units and measuring equipment to estimate, then measure, a capacity.**

Lesson context
Provide opportunities for children to estimate and measure the capacity of different containers with a range of standard or non-standard units. Encourage the children to explain why they used a particular unit and to say whether it was suitable.

Setting the homework
Explain the activity to the children. Ask them to bring the completed sheet back to school.

Back at school
Using an A3 enlargement of the homework sheet discuss which units would be suitable for measuring which container. Ask the children to justify their decisions.

p124 TIME ORDER · MATHS TO SHARE

Learning outcome
- Understand and use the vocabulary related to time. Order familiar events in time. Read the time to the hour or half hour on analogue clocks.

Lesson context
Provide opportunities for the children to use their clock faces to show both o'clock and half hour times.

Setting the homework
Explain the activity to the children. Discuss with them what time they get up in the morning, eat their lunch and go to bed at night. Remind them that different people do these things at different times.

Back at school
Using an A3 enlargement of the homework sheet, ask the children for suggestions of which time belongs to which picture.

p125 THE WEEK AND THE SEASONS · MATHS TO SHARE

Learning outcome
- Understand and use the vocabulary related to time. Order familiar events in time. Know the days of the week and the seasons of the year.

Lesson context
Provide opportunities for reciting the days of the week in order and then to answer questions such as: *What day is it today? What day will it be tomorrow? Which days are at the weekend?* Talk about the seasons and show the children pictures representing typical seasonal weather.

Setting the homework
Explain the activity to the children. Ask them to bring the sheet back to school when it is finished.

Back at school
Mark the homework. Decide if children with errors would benefit from further experience of this work.

p126 ABOUT ME · MATHS TO SHARE

Learning outcome
- **Use mental strategies to solve simple problems** set in measuring contexts, **using counting, addition, subtraction, doubling and halving, explaining methods and reasoning orally.**

Lesson context
Set some word problems that involve measures. Use all of the measures including time. The problems can include: *The pencils are five cubes long. How long would three pencils be? How many hours are there from 1 o'clock to 7 o'clock?* Encourage the children to use their mental strategies to solve the problems and to explain their solution strategies.

Setting the homework
Explain the activity to the children. Talk about the times when they do different things, such as getting up in the morning, having breakfast and watching television. Explain that not everyone will do these things at exactly the same time. Ask the children to bring their sheets back to school when they are completed.

Back at school
Mark the homework. Decide whether to make an 'About me' book with the sheets as part of a display on 'Time'.

p127 HOW MANY?
MATHS TO SHARE

Learning outcome
• Solve a given problem by sorting, classifying and organizing information in simple ways, such as: using objects or pictures; in a list or simple table. Discuss and explain results.

Lesson context
Set some problems to be solved where the collected data can be recorded using either objects, pictures, a list or a simple table. Problems can include: *Who has a first name which has less than five letters? Who is your favourite pop star?* When the data has been collected and recorded, ask questions such as: *How many... ? Which is the most popular?*

Setting the homework
Explain the activity to the children. Explain that they can ask their family and friends to help with this. Ask them to bring the sheets back to school when they are completed.

Back at school
Use the data from some of the homework sheets to ask questions such as: *In Harpreet's family who held the most pegs? How many more did her dad hold than her mum?*

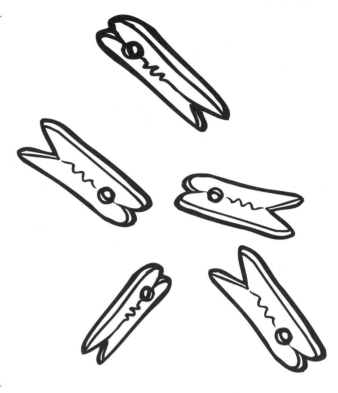

p128 WHAT CAN WE TELL?
MATHS TO SHARE

Learning outcome
• Solve a given problem by sorting, classifying and organizing information in simple ways, such as: using objects or pictures; in a list or simple table. Discuss and explain results.

Lesson context
Set some problems to be solved where the collected data can be recorded using objects, pictures, a list or a simple table. Problems can include: *Who has a first name which has less than five letters? Who is your favourite pop star?* When the data has been collected and recorded, ask questions such as: *How many ...? Which is the most popular?*

Setting the homework
Explain the activity to the children. Ask them to bring the completed sheets back to school.

Back at school
Mark the homework. Decide whether children who had errors need further experience of interpreting results.

Our pets

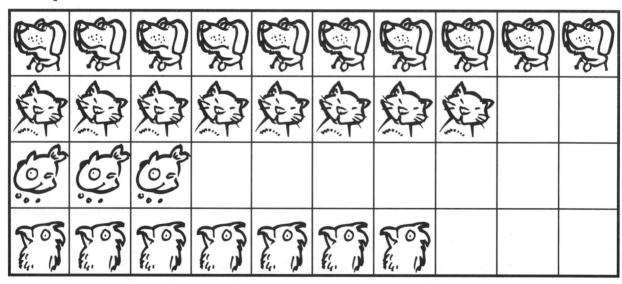

Counting

- Say the rhyme together.
- Do the actions together.

One, two, buckle my shoe.

Three, four, knock at the door.

Five, six, pick up sticks.

Seven, eight, lay them straight.

Nine, ten, a big fat hen.

Eleven, twelve, dig and delve.
Thirteen, fourteen, maids a-courting.
Fifteen, sixteen, maids in the kitchen
Seventeen, eighteen, maids in waiting.
Nineteen, twenty, my plate's empty.

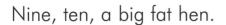

- Say or sing some other counting rhymes.

Dear Helper,

This activity is intended to help your child know the number names in order. Say or sing the number rhyme together and encourage your child to do the actions. Then, count up to 10 and back to zero. As your child becomes more confident with counting, count up to 20 and back to zero, then to 30, and so on. Use opportunities for counting together, e.g., going up or down stairs, or when out walking. Count to a rhythm, perhaps while swinging your arms in time together.

Name:

Counters

- Count to 10 together.

- Count out ten counters.

- Put some of them inside the garden.

- Count how many.

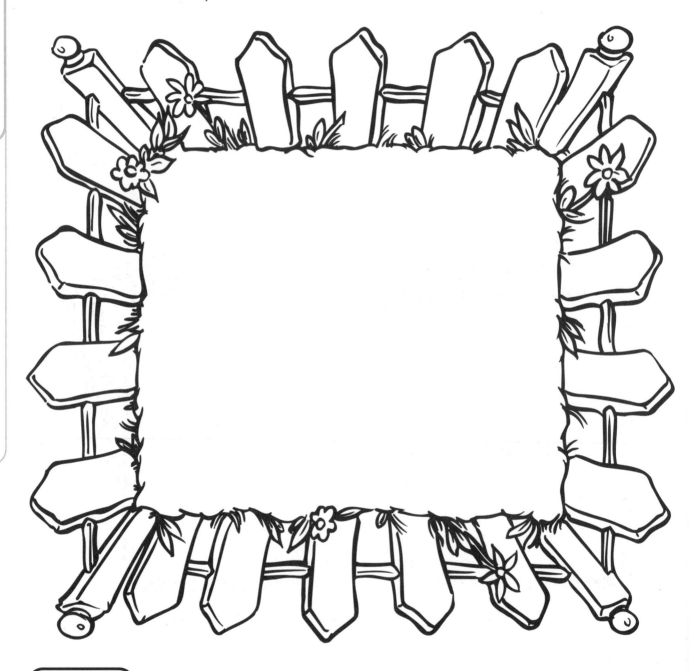

Dear Helper,

This activity is designed to help your child count accurately. You will need ten counters (buttons, pennies or little bits of paper will do). Encourage your child to touch, count and move each counter as they count them. This shows which have been counted and which are still to be counted. If your child gets stuck, count each counter together slowly, touching and moving it. Say, for the sixth counter: *We counted to six. There are six counters.*

Name:

Numeral snap

Two people can play this game.
Use a pack of playing cards.

- Put the cards face down on their space.

- Take turns to turn over a card on to your pile, face up.

- When the top card on each pile shows the same number, the first person to say, 'Snap', collects the other person's pile.

- Carry on turning over the cards.

Put the pack here, face down.

The winner is the one who gets all the cards.

Dear Helper,

This activity is designed to help your child read numbers. Use a pack of playing cards with the picture cards removed or two sets of cards each with the numbers 1 to 10 written on them. As you play 'Snap', ask your child to say the numbers on the cards. Encourage them to read the numbers. If they are not sure, then count the pips if using the playing cards. This game can be played by all the family. Challenge your child by making just one pile of discarded cards and encourage them to remember the previous card.

Name:

Number track

You will need: a dice, and a friend to play this game with you.

- Throw the dice.
  Start on that number.

- Throw the dice again.
  Count on that many.

- Let your partner have a turn.

- Whoever lands on the higher number, colours a star.

- Go back to the Start.

- Have some more turns.

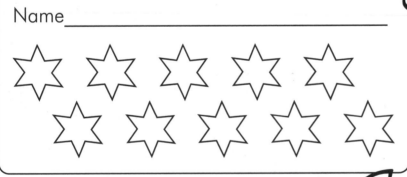

Name_____

Name_____

Who coloured the most stars?

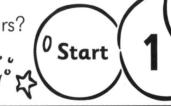

Dear Helper,

This activity is intended to help your child to order numbers. Check that they count on by moving to the next shape for a count of 'one' and so on. Ask your child to read the numbers on the track and the scores on the dice, both for their turn and for yours. When they are really confident at this game, play it in reverse, counting back from 7, 8, 9 or 10 for a throw of the dice.

Name:

Making sums

- Choose two of these numbers.

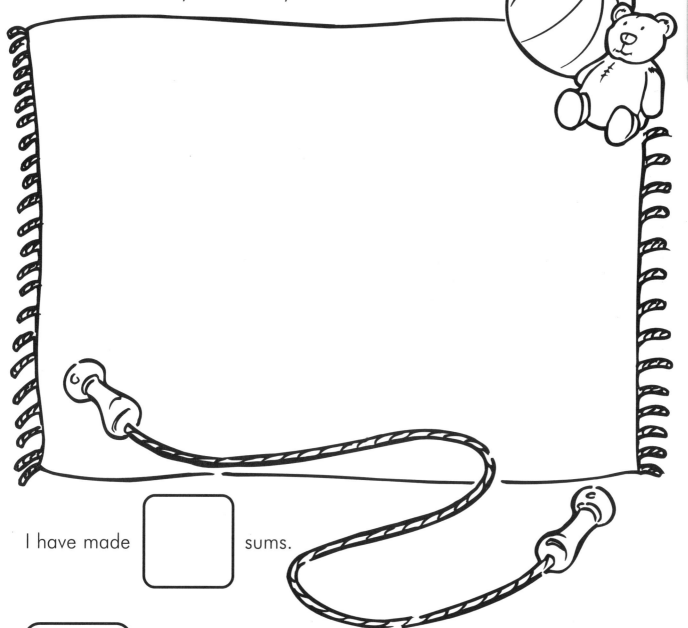

| 1 | 2 | 3 | 4 |

- Write an add sum. What is the total?
  See how many add sums you can make.

I have made ⬜ sums.

Name:

Coin recognition

- Each choose a coin from the bag.
  Are the coins the same?
  What are the coins called?

- Put each coin on to its moneybox.

Dear Helper,

This activity helps your child to recognise coins. Put some 1p, 2p, 5p and 10p coins into a bag. Ask your child to take a coin and you take one. Compare them. Are they the same? Ask your child to name the coins. If your child finds this difficult, talk about the colour of the coins and their size. When your child is confident with this, put some 20p, 50p, £1 and £2 coins into the bag and repeat the activity. Relabel the moneyboxes if you wish.

Name:

Shopping

You will need: some 1p, 2p and 5p coins.

- Choose a toy. Choose coins to pay for it.
- Choose different coins to pay for it.

How many different ways can you find?

Dear Helper,

This activity helps your child to recognise coins and to use combinations of coins to pay for something. At first your child may choose to use 1p coins. Encourage them to use other coins and to count their value. For example, if paying 4p, your child could use 2p and 2p, and count this as: *2p and 1p makes 3p and 1p makes 4p.* As your child becomes more confident, encourage the use of 5p coins too.

5 and a bit

- Spin a paperclip on the spinner.

- Say the number that it lands on.

- Make the number into '5 and a bit'.

- Add your number to 5.

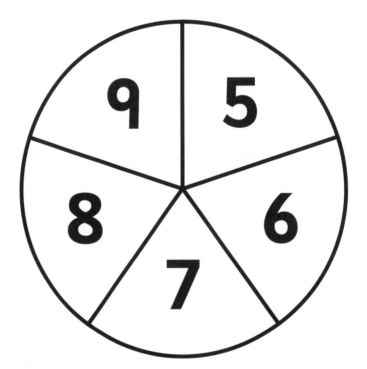

Dear Helper,

Your child will need a paperclip and a pencil to do this activity and may need some counters or pennies. The activity helps your child to break down a number between 5 and 10 into '5 and a bit'. For example, 8 is 5 and 3. If your child finds this hard, let them use some counters and break the number into a five and a 'bit', then count all to recombine. When your child is confident with this, ask them to add their number to 5. So for 5 add 8 they would say: *5 and 5 is 10, and 3 is 13.*

Name:

Matching pair

0	1	2	3
zero	**one**	**two**	**three**

4	5	6
four	**five**	**six**

7	8	9	10
seven	**eight**	**nine**	**ten**

- Cut out the cards and shuffle them.

- Place each card face down on the table.

- Take turns to turn over and read two cards.

- When you find a matching pair, keep those cards.

- If they don't match, put them face down again.

- The person with the most pairs of cards is the winner.

Dear Helper,

This game helps your child to read numbers and number words. Ask your child to read both cards for each turn and then ask them: *Are these the same number?* Encourage your child to remember where they have seen the same number before. If your child finds this hard, limit the cards initially to 1 to 5. Challenge your child by making cards for the numbers 11 to 15 and play the game again.

Name:

Tens and ones

- Stack 20 pennies in a pile on the '1p' circle and place a 10p coin in the other circle.

- Take some of the pennies off the pile and spread them out in the box.

- Count them.

- Now, change 10 of the pennies in the box so that you have a 10p coin and some 1p coins.

How much do you have?

Dear Helper,

This activity helps your child to understand that 'teens' numbers are made up of a ten and some ones. If your child finds this hard, then help them to count all of the coins, then to count them again, moving ten of them to one side. These can then be exchanged for a 10p coin. Say together, for 17: *17 is the same as 10 and 7*. Challenge your child to take more pennies and to make a number between 20 and 30, using more 10p coins.

7p problem

You will need: a pencil and some 1p, 2p and 5p coins.
I have 7p in my pocket.
Which coins might I have?

- Draw the coins in a purse.

- Find three more ways of doing this.

Dear Helper,

This activity is intended to help your child recognise coins and combine them to make totals. Ask your child to say what each coin is worth. To get started, you could count out seven 1p coins and ask your child to exchange these for 2p coins, then include a 5p coin. Total the coins by counting on: *2p and 2p is 4p and 2p is 6p and 1p is 7p.* Challenge your child by repeating the activity for 8p. Ask: *Which way uses the least number of coins? How did you work it out?*

Name:

Longer and shorter

- Choose some toys.

- Compare them with this brush.
  Say how the toy is different from the brush.

- Draw a picture of each toy in the box
  with the correct label.

wider	longer

narrower	shorter

Dear Helper,

Your child needs to be able to use and understand words about length. Begin this activity with just two toys and ask your child to compare them for length. If your child doesn't know how to do this, check together that one end of each toy is lined up with the brush drawn on the sheet and then compare the other ends. As a further challenge, try comparing three toys and ask your child to put them in order, using words such as 'longest', 'shortest', 'widest' and 'narrowest'.

Name:

Picture ruler

- Find things that you estimate are about 8 pictures long.
- Use the picture ruler to measure.
- Fill in the chart.

I chose	I was about right. ✓ ✗

Dear Helper,

This activity is designed to help your child estimate and measure length. Your child may find it easier if they cut the picture ruler carefully away from the recording chart. Ask your child to look around the room and think of things that are about 8 pictures long. Ask your child to check by measuring. Make sure that they carefully line up the edge of the picture ruler with the item to be measured. Your child can complete the chart and put a tick or a cross to show whether they estimated reasonably accurately or not. Challenge your child to find things that are 6 pictures long or 2 pictures long and so on.

Name:

Shape search

- Look at the pictures.

- Find some things with the same shape.

- Draw the things you find in their box.

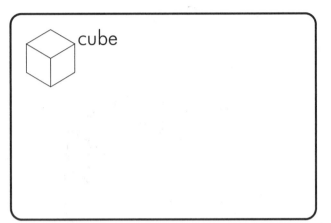
cube

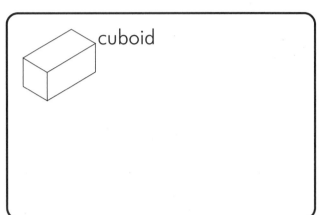
cuboid

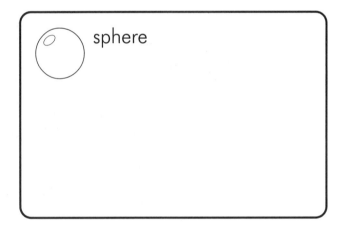
sphere

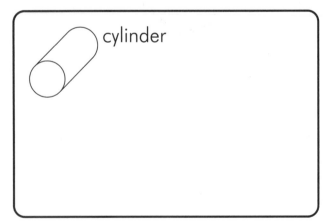
cylinder

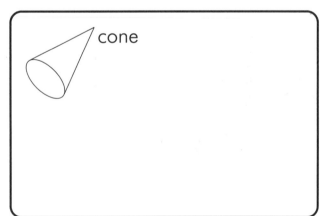
cone

Dear Helper,

This activity helps your child to recognise shapes and read their names. Encourage your child to find several examples for each shape. If they are unsure of the mathematical name of a shape, read it for them. Challenge your child by asking them to shut their eyes and hold one of their objects. Ask them to feel the shape and name it from what they can feel. Emphasise that the shapes are called the same thing whichever way up they are.

Name:

Build a model

- Make a model like the one in the picture.

- Look at your model.
  How is it the same as the one in the picture?
  How is it different?

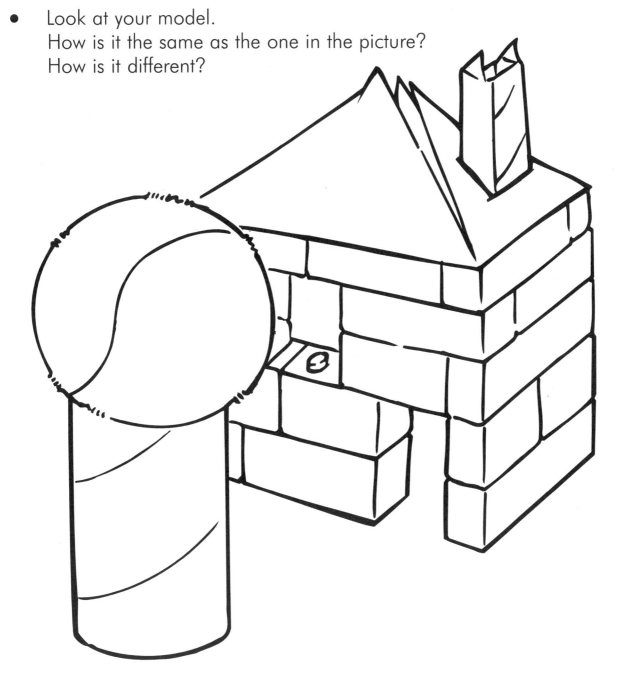

Dear Helper,

This activity is designed to help your child recognise 3-D shapes in pictures. Your child can use any building materials: a construction kit, bricks or 'junk' materials such as cardboard tubes and boxes. Encourage your child to copy the picture and to explain why they have chosen the particular shapes to make the model. When it is finished, discuss how the model is the same as the picture and how it is different. Different is 'OK' too. Challenge your child to draw their own picture and then to make a model of it.

Name:

Build a tower

- Use some building materials.

- Build a tower.

- Draw a picture of it.
  Make your picture as much like your model as you can.

Dear Helper,

This activity is intended to help your child draw 3-D shapes accurately. Your child can use a construction kit, bricks or 'junk' materials such as cardboard boxes and sticky tape. Encourage your child to build their model carefully and as they build it, ask questions such as: *What if we use this piece instead? What could we change?* When the model is complete, ask your child to draw a picture of it. Encourage them to look carefully at each piece and to draw them as accurately as they can. Please send the completed picture back to school.

Number rhymes

- Say some favourite number rhymes.
- Use this number line to help you to count in tens.

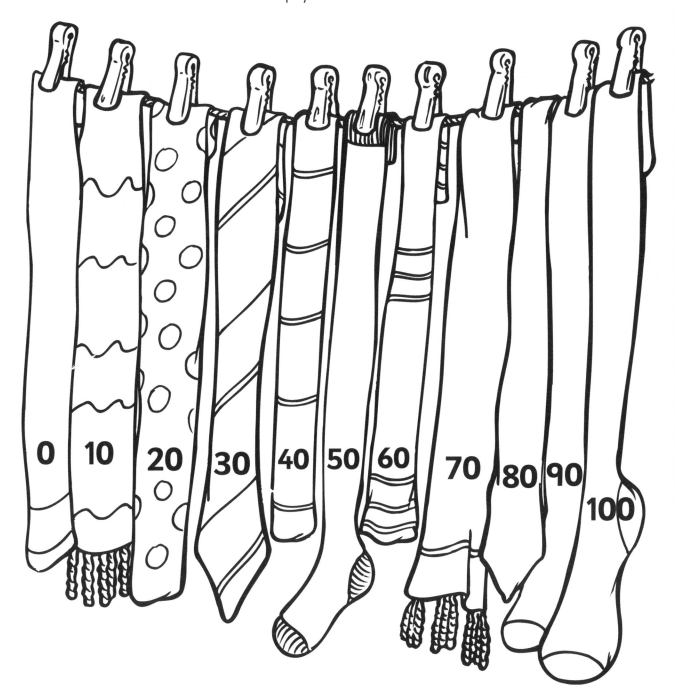

0 10 20 30 40 50 60 70 80 90 100

Dear Helper,

This activity is designed to help your child count in ones and tens. Begin by saying or singing together some favourite number rhymes. Ask your child to teach you a new one that they have learned at school. Now point to the numbers on the number line, starting with zero and say them in order: *zero, ten, twenty,... one hundred*. Now say the numbers going backwards from 100 to zero. 'Skip count' along the number line: *zero, ten, twenty, ten, twenty, thirty, twenty, thirty, forty...eighty, ninety, one hundred*. Say the numbers in a rhythm. Challenge your child to 'skip count' backwards: *one hundred, ninety, eighty, ninety, eighty, seventy....*

Name:

Picture count

- Count how many insects there are in each box.
- Write how many there are in the little box.

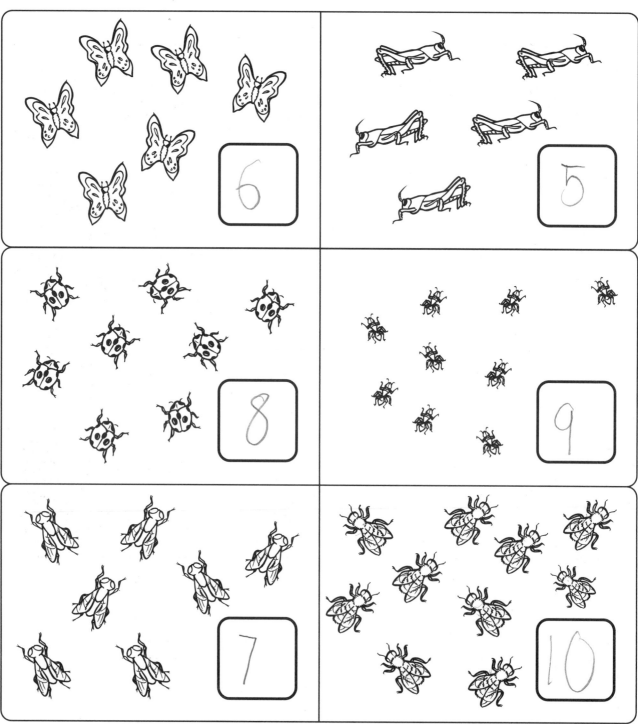

Dear Helper,

This activity helps your child to count how many and to write the number. Ask your child to point to each small picture as they count. Check that they don't count any small picture twice or miss any. Encourage them to write how many as a number. If your child has difficulty with writing the number, write it for them so that they can trace over it. Challenge your child to draw their own pictures on the back of the sheet and write how many.

Name:

Number add

- Find two boxes which total 16.

- Write the add sum.

- Find four different ways of doing this.

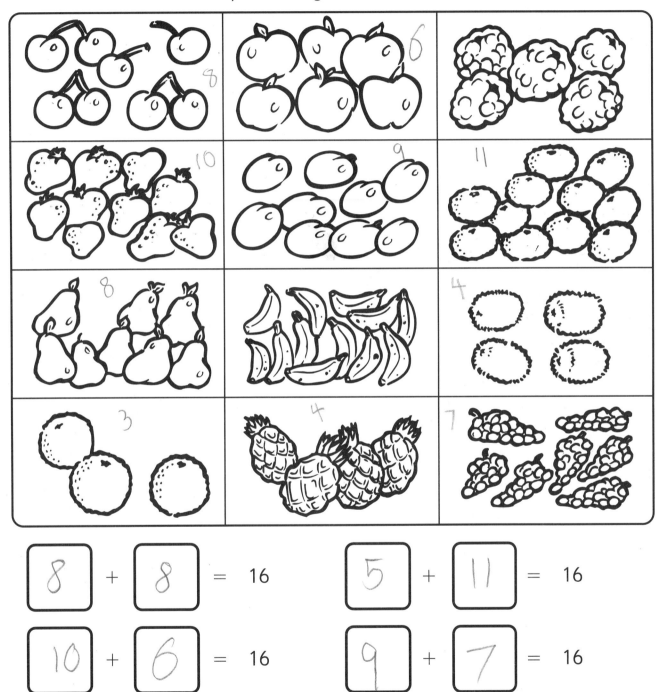

| 8 | + | 8 | = 16 | | 5 | + | 11 | = 16 |

| 10 | + | 6 | = 16 | | 9 | + | 7 | = 16 |

Dear Helper,

This activity helps your child to solve problems. Begin by asking your child to count how many there are in each box. Now ask them to find two boxes which total 16. If your child finds this difficult, encourage them to count on from one box to another: *8 and 9, 10, 11, 12, 13, 14, 15, 16. So, 8 and 8 are 16.* Encourage your child to find different ways of doing this and to write the sums. Challenge your child to find combinations using three numbers and to write sums for these on the back of the sheet.

Name:

Pick up 15

You will need: about 30 counters or pennies.
Take turns with your Helper.

- Take a handful of counters.

- Count how many.

- Have you picked up 15?

- Try each time to pick up just 15.

- Colour in a star each time you pick up 15.

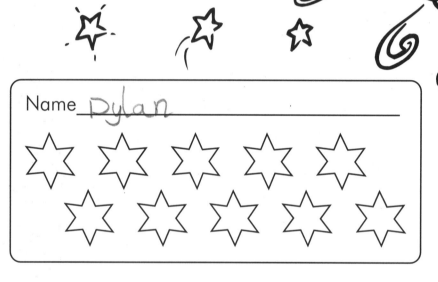

Name _Dylan_

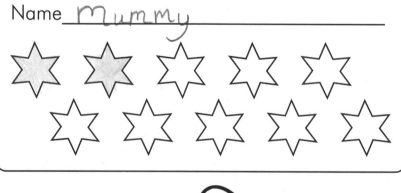

Name _mummy_

Dear Helper,

This activity helps your child to estimate with increasing accuracy. This can be played as a game. Take turns to pick up about 15 counters without counting. Spread the counters out on the sheet and count them. Every time you pick up the correct amount, colour in a star in the box. The first person to colour five stars wins the game. If your child finds this difficult, reduce the number of counters to be picked up to eight. Challenge your child to pick up 20 counters.

Name:

Hand number

- Put your hand on the paper and draw around it.
- Fill your hand outline with counters.
- Count them.

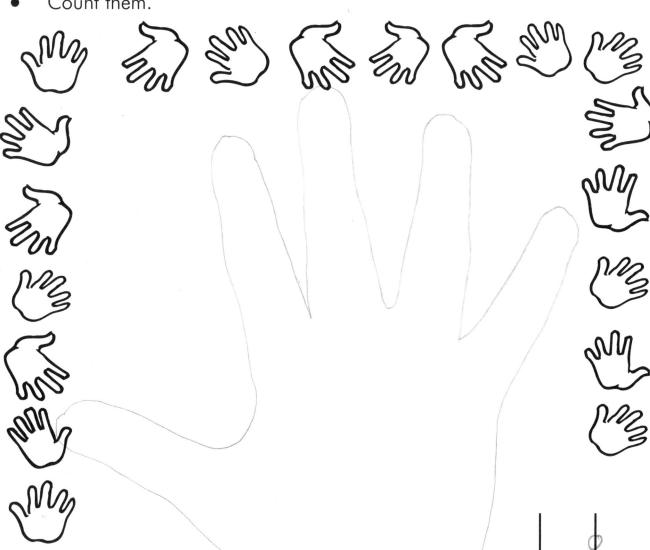

Draw beads on this abacus to show how many counters.

Dear Helper,

This activity is intended to help your child understand tens and units numbers. Your child will need some large counters or buttons. If your child finds it difficult to draw the outline of their own hand, do this for them. When they have filled the outline with counters, ask your child to count how many counters there are and to draw beads to represent this number on the abacus. For example, for 15, they would draw one bead on the ten spike and five on the units spike. Challenge your child to draw around the outline of the hand of other family members on further pieces of paper and record the number of counters needed to fill them in the same way.

Name:

Dice throw

You will need: a dice and a counter each.

- Take turns to throw the dice and move your counter around the game board.

- If you land on a sum, work out the answer.

Finish	Start	5 + 6			5 + 9
8 + 9					
7 + 9					5 + 8
6 + 9					5 + 7
	7 + 8		6 + 8		6 + 7

Dear Helper,

This activity helps your child to use the strategy of 'partitioning' numbers to add them. When adding 6, 7, 8 or 9, encourage your child to split the number into '5 and a bit'. For example, for 5 + 8, this would be 5 + 5 + 3 = 10 + 3 = 13; and for 6 + 8 this would be 5 + 1 + 5 + 3 = 5 + 5 + 1 + 3 = 10 + 4 = 14. Encourage your child to work out the sums on which each of you land. The winner is the one to reach the finish square first. If your child finds it hard to work out the sums, then write down each sum in the expanded form as shown above and work out each stage together.

Name:

Fruit shopping

- Choose two or three fruits that cost a total of 15p.
- Find different ways.
- Write your choices as sums.

Recording

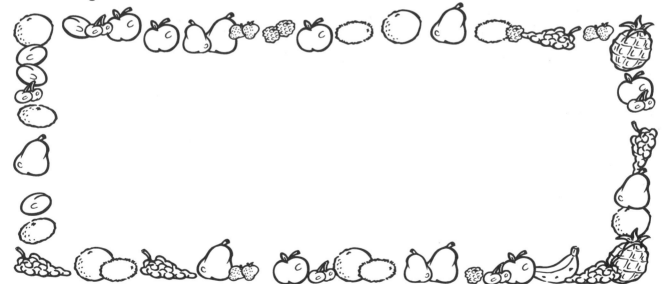

Dear Helper,

This activity helps your child to use the strategy of making 6, 7, 8 or 9 into '5 and a bit' when adding. For example, for 6p + 9p: 5p + 1p + 5p + 4p = 5p + 5p + 1p + 4p = 10p + 5p = 15p. Encourage your child to find different ways of combining two or three prices to make 15p. If your child finds this difficult, write each sum as shown above and work through it together. Challenge your child to make different totals, such as 16p, 18p or 20p.

PHOTOCOPIABLE

Name:

Double or double add one

You will need: a coin and the number cards from a pack of playing cards.

- Take a playing card.

- Toss the coin.
  Heads means double the card number.
  Tails means add the card number to one more than the card number.

- Write a sum for each card.

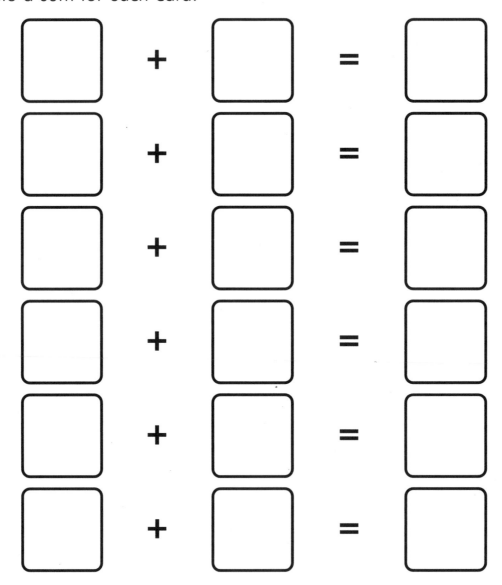

Dear Helper,

This activity helps your child to use the strategy of using known double facts to find 'near doubles'. So, for 5 + 6, this can be seen as 5 + 5 + 1. Encourage your child to explain the strategy as they carry out the activity and to record the sums in the boxes. If your child finds this activity difficult, encourage them to count on in ones from the card number: *5 and 6, 7, 8, 9, 10, 11*. If your child wishes to write more of these sums, then they can write them on the back of the sheet.

Name:

Take away

- Choose two of these numbers.
- Write a take away sum.
- Write the answer.
  How many different take away sums can you find?

| 1 | 3 | 4 | 6 | 7 |

Dear Helper,

This activity is to help your child understand 'taking away'. If your child finds this difficult, draw a number line with numbers from 1 to 10 and encourage them to use the number line to count back from the larger to the smaller number. For example, for 6 – 3: 5, 4, 3: *6 take away 3 is 3*. Challenge your child to make take away sums using the numbers 2, 4, 5, 6, 8.

Name:

Under the tub

You will need: some counters or coins and a tub or cup.

- Count out 8 counters.
- Ask your Helper to hide some under the tub. How many are hidden?
- Write a subtraction sum.
- Repeat until you have five sums.

☐ – ☐ = ☐

☐ – ☐ = ☐

☐ – ☐ = ☐

☐ – ☐ = ☐

☐ – ☐ = ☐

Dear Helper,

This activity helps your child use addition to help them solve a subtraction problem. When you have hidden some of the counters ask: *How many counters are hidden under the tub?* If your child finds this difficult, encourage them to count on from the counters that they can see, so for five counters that they can see, they say: *6, 7, 8. There are three counters hidden. 8 – 5 = 3.* Ask your child to record this as a subtraction number sentence. Challenge your child to repeat this with nine counters this time, recording any subtractions on the back of this sheet.

Giving change

- Choose some sweets to buy.

- Pretend you have 10p to spend.
  Will you have change? If so, how much?

- Buy some more sweets with 10p.

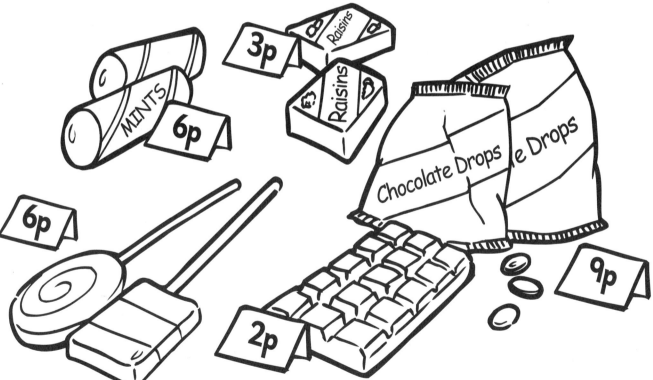

Dear Helper,

This activity helps your child to work out the change by counting on from the price to the amount of money given. If your child finds this difficult, use real coins to help. You act as the shopkeeper and let your child give you 10p. Count out the change into their hand, counting on from the price. For a lolly say: *7p, 8p. 9p, 10p. That is 4p change. So, 10p take away 6p is 4p.* When they are confident, ask them to count out the change into your hand. Challenge your child to buy two items and count out the change from 20p.

Making 10p

- Find a way to make 10p exactly.
- Write an addition sum which totals 10p.
- Find six different ways.

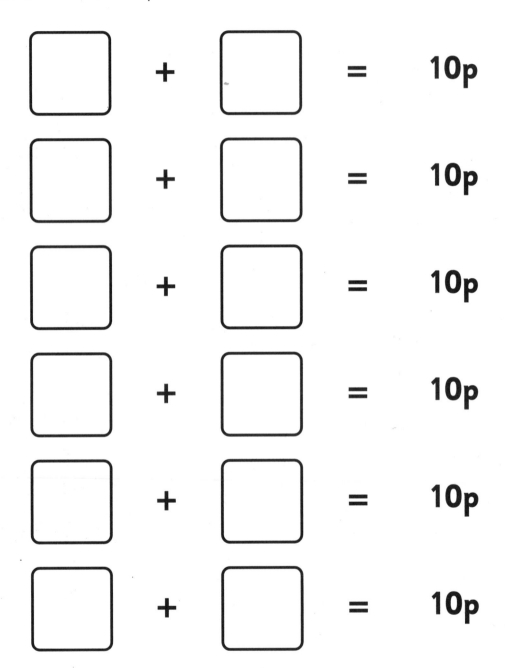

$$\square + \square = \mathbf{10p}$$

$$\square + \square = \mathbf{10p}$$

$$\square + \square = \mathbf{10p}$$

$$\square + \square = \mathbf{10p}$$

$$\square + \square = \mathbf{10p}$$

$$\square + \square = \mathbf{10p}$$

Dear Helper,

This activity helps your child to total amounts of money. If your child finds this difficult, use coins to help. Put out ten 1p coins and ask your child to put the coins into two separate piles, then count how many in each. So, for 4p and 6p, ask your child to write the sum 4p + 6p = 10p. Repeat for other totals to 10p. Then, use other coins which total 10p, such as 2p, 2p, 1p, 5p. Challenge your child to find more than six possible sums and to work without using coins.

Name:

Sequencing

You will need: scissors, paper, adhesive or sticky tape.

- Cut out the pictures.
- Put them in order.
- Stick them on to another sheet of paper in order.

Dear Helper,

This activity helps your child to put events in order. Talk about things that you do at home, such as going shopping, and encourage your child to say what happens first, then next and so on. Ask your child to cut out the pictures from the sheet and spread them out. Encourage them to tell the story in the pictures, putting them in order. If your child find this hard, talk about what the pictures show. Challenge your child to draw some pictures of a different event, such as preparing a meal, and to put them in order so that they tell a story. Send your child's drawings back to school.

Name:

Telling the time

- Talk about the pictures.

- Set your clock to the time you do the things in each picture.

Dear Helper,

This activity helps your child to tell the time. Either use a real clock with hands or a cardboard clock face with hands that move. Talk about the pictures and ask your child to set the clock for the time that they do each of the things in the pictures. If your child finds this hard, cut out the pictures and order them by time, together. Challenge your child to show on the clock face other important times, such as 'home time' and going to bed.

Name:

What can you do in 1 minute?

- Use a clock which measures time in minutes.

- How many times can you do these things in 1 minute?

- Estimate, then count.

	I think I'll do...	In 1 minute, I did...
Build a tower with five bricks.		
Write your name.		
Do up your shoes.		
Skip.		
Stand up and sit down again.		

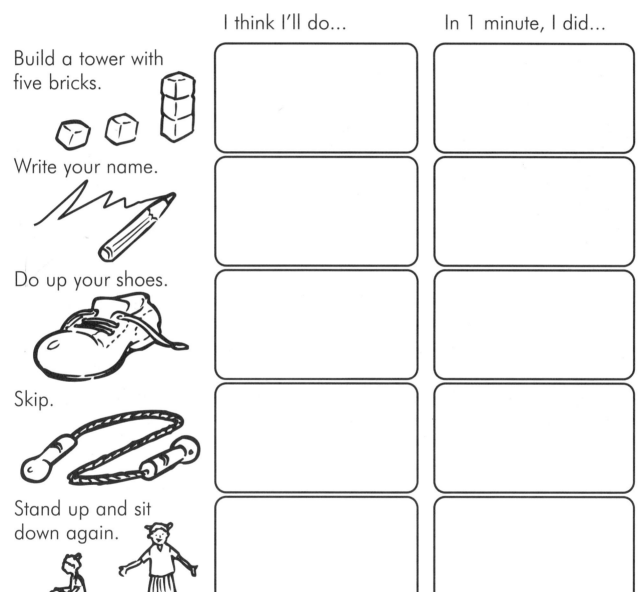

Dear Helper,

This activity helps your child to estimate time passing. You will need a clock with a second hand. Explain to your child how to tell when a minute has passed by using the second hand on the clock. Ask them to estimate how many times they can build a tower with five bricks, then to check by building it. Repeat this for the other suggestions. If preferred this could be a family activity and everyone could take part. Challenge your child to think of other things that they could do in 1 minute, and to check this by trying them out.

Favourite fruits

- Ask your family to help you.
- Find out which fruit each person likes best.
- Put a tick in the box for their favourite.

Name	cherries	apples	oranges	pears	bananas

Dear Helper,

This activity helps your child to sort and record information. Ask other family members and friends to help. Encourage your child to ask the questions and to put a tick in the correct box for each family member. If your child finds this difficult, write the family member's name for your child and ask your child just to put the tick in the correct box. Challenge your child to decide on other information which they could collect and to make another chart for it.

Name:

Comparing

Look at objects in your home.

- Find things that are taller than you.
- Find things that are shorter than you.
- Find things about the same height as you.
- Draw them.

Taller than me	About the same height as me	Shorter than me

Dear Helper,

This activity helps your child to compare things for length. Encourage your child to look around the house for things with which they can compare with their own height. If they find the comparison difficult, hold a mirror so that your child can see the lengths. Challenge your child to compare the height of another member of the family or a friend with items at home and to find things that are about the same height.

Name:

How tall is a chair?

Look at the chairs at home.

- Draw them.

- Put a tick by the one that you think is the tallest.

- Check by measuring the chairs, using bricks or books to measure. Did you make a good estimate?

Dear Helper,

This activity helps your child to estimate and measure. Together, find some things that are the same length that could be used for measuring by putting them end to end. These could be books or large toy bricks. Ask your child first to estimate which is the tallest chair, then check by measuring. They can write the measure against each drawing to help to check which is the tallest. Challenge your child to estimate and measure the lowest table in the house and repeat the activity. They can record on the back of the sheet.

Name:

Odds and evens

You will need: two sets of coloured counters and a dice.

- Throw the dice and move your counter.
  If you land on an even number, take two counters.
  If you land on an odd number, take one counter.

- Now it is your friend's turn.
  The player with the most counters at the end of the game
  is the winner.

Start	9	6	3	7	10

2
13

19	15	8	4	20	18

14
1

5	17	12	11	16	Finish

Dear Helper,

This activity helps your child to recognise odd and even numbers. You will need a dice and some counters or buttons. If your child finds it difficult to recognise whether a number is odd or even, ask them to count out that number in counters and to count these in twos. If the count finishes on the number of counters, then it is an even number. If one more is needed/left over, then it is odd. Challenge your child further by asking them to answer quickly without using counters.

Name:

Decade number search

Look at home for some tens numbers.

- Write the numbers in the chart and say where you found them.

- Find six examples.

- Take the sheet back to school when you have finished.

My tens numbers	I found my numbers here

Dear Helper,

This activity helps your child to recognise tens numbers, such as 10, 20, 30.... Encourage your child to use the picture clues to find some numbers. If your child finds this difficult look together at, for example, a book, and find the tens page numbers. You may need to help them to write the numbers and where these were found on to the chart. Challenge your child to think of other places where they could find tens numbers, such as on packets and tins.

Grid cover

Play this game with a friend.

- Make a tens and units number.
  Spin the paper clip on the Tens spinner.
  Spin the paper clip on the Units spinner.

- Cover your tens and units number on the board with a counter.
  The winner is the one with the most counters at the end of the game.

tens

10   20

0

ones

0 1 2 3 4 5 6 7 8 9

0	1	2	3	4	5	6
7	8	9	10	11	12	13
14	15	16	17	18	19	20

Dear Helper,

This activity helps your child to recognise that 'teens' numbers are made from a ten and some units (or 'ones'). You will need several counters or buttons in two different colours, a pencil and a paper clip. If your child finds this activity difficult, discuss that, for example: *One ten and four units make 14; no tens and four units make 4.* Challenge your child to say what two tens and some units would make, for example: *Two tens and four units make 24.*

Name:

10 more, 10 less

- Write the number that is 10 less.

- Write the number that is 10 more.

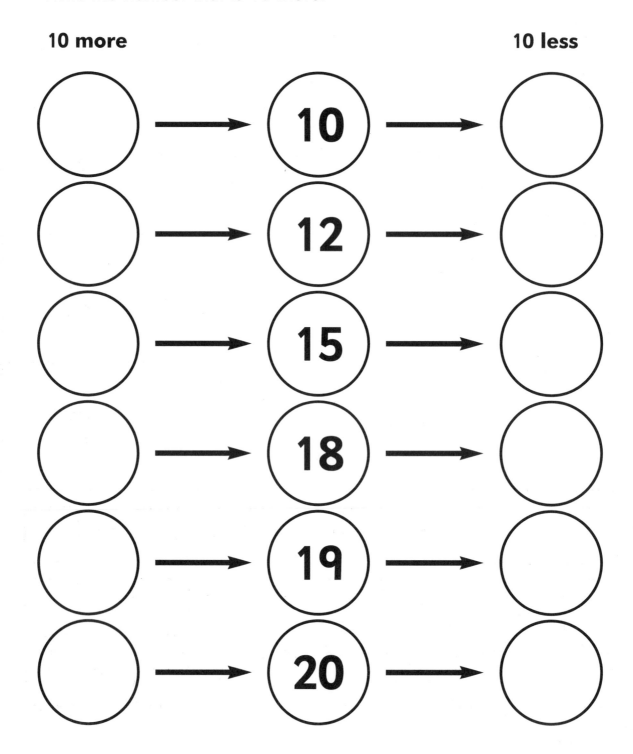

10 more

10 less

Dear Helper,

This activity helps your child to recognise numbers that are 10 more or less than a given number. Ask your child to count in tens from the starting number, forwards first for two or three tens, then back. For example, for the starting number 16 say: *16, 26, 36*. Then: *16, 6*. Challenge your child to make up some more '10 more, 10 less' examples and to write these on the back of the sheet.

100 MATHS HOMEWORK ACTIVITIES • YEAR 1 TERM 2

Counter toss

Find two counters, pennies or buttons.

- Toss them on to this number grid.

- Write a difference sum with your numbers.
  Put the larger number first.

- Find the difference between the two numbers.

1	2	3	4
5	6	7	8
9	10	11	12

☐ - ☐ = ☐   ☐ - ☐ = ☐

☐ - ☐ = ☐   ☐ - ☐ = ☐

☐ - ☐ = ☐   ☐ - ☐ = ☐

Dear Helper,

This activity helps your child to understand what is meant by 'difference'. For example, the difference between 5 and 7 is 2, or 7 – 5 = 2. If your child finds this difficult, use some counters to help. Put out the first number in counters in a row, then the second number underneath so that they can see which number has more and how many more. Ask your child to write the sum. For 5 and 7, your child would see that 7 has two more, and would write 7 – 5 = 2. Challenge your child to write some more difference sums on the back of the sheet in the same way.

Name:

Difference of 6

- Find pairs of numbers with a difference of 6.
- Write the numbers in these number sentences.

 – = **6**

 – = **6**

 – = **6**

 – = **6**

 – = **6**

 – = **6**

Dear Helper,

This activity helps your child to understand that difference is a form of subtraction. For example, the difference between 3 and 9, or 9 and 3, is 6. If your child finds this difficult, start with a smaller difference such as 3 and ask them to find example sums with that difference, such as 6 – 3 = 3. Challenge your child to find more numbers with a difference of 6, using 'teen' numbers. These can be written on the back of the sheet.

Name:

Prices

- Roll a dice.
- Move your counter that number of squares.
- Decide which coins to use to pay for the toy on your square.
- Let your Helper play too.
- Roll the dice and count on again.

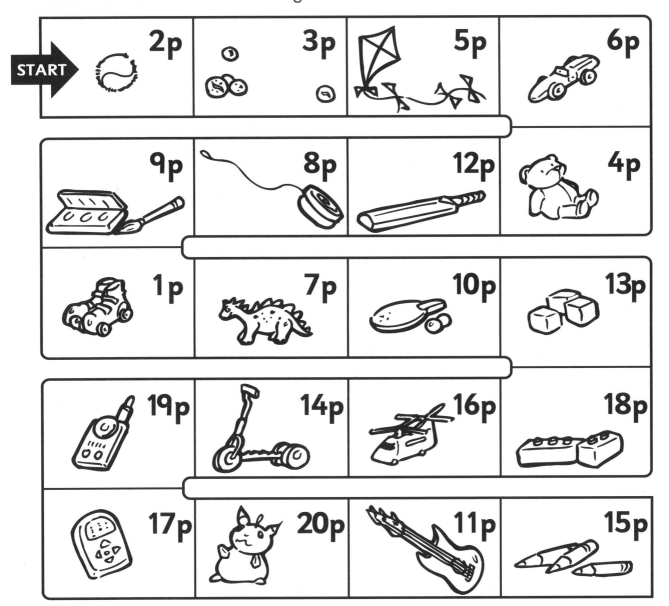

START 2p 3p 5p 6p

9p 8p 12p 4p

1p 7p 10p 13p

19p 14p 16p 18p

17p 20p 11p 15p

Dear Helper,

This activity helps your child to decide how to pay for things using the exact money. You will need a dice, a counter for each player and some 1p, 2p, 5p and 10p coins. If your child uses all 1p coins to pay for something, ask them to think about other coins that they could use. For example, if something costs 8p, then suggest that they start with a 5p coin, and then counts on: *5p and 2p is 7p, and 1p is 8p. We need a 5p, a 2p and a 1p coin.* Challenge your child to find the least number of coins needed to pay for the item each time.

Shopping

- Choose something to buy.
- Give change from 10p.
- Repeat for buying other things.

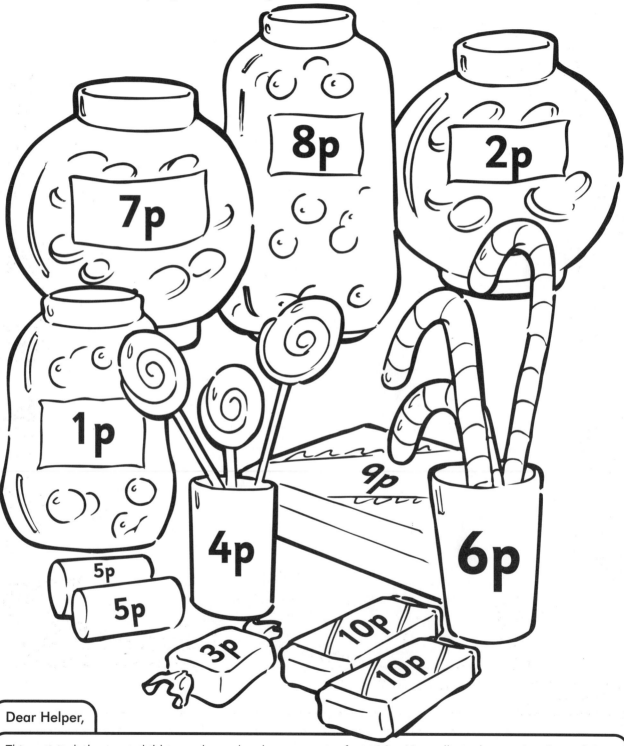

Dear Helper,

This activity helps your child to work out the change to give from 10p. You will need some 1p, 2p and 5p coins and a 10p coin. Ask your child to be the shopper to begin with. Ask them to choose an item to buy and give you 10p. You count out the change into their hand. When your child understands what to do, change roles. If your child counts out the change in 1p coins, work together to see what other coins could be used. Challenge your child to use the least possible number of coins to give change.

8p

- Find different ways to pay 8p.

- Write these as addition sums.

- Find six ways.

Dear Helper,

Your child needs to realise that the same amount of money can be made up from different combinations of coins. You will need some 1p, 2p and 5p coins for this activity. Ask your child to find a way of making 8p, then to record this as an addition sum, for example 5p + 2p + 1p = 8p. If your child just counts out eight 1p coins, work together to find other ways. Count the coins together, for example: *2p and 2p is 4p, adding another 2p makes 6p and adding another 2p makes 8p. So 2p add 2p add 2p add 2p is 8p.* Challenge your child to find different ways of making 9p.

Name:

Totals 10

- Make three totals of 10 using two numbers.
- Make three totals of 10 using three numbers.

Dear Helper,

Often children do not realise that more than two numbers can be added together. Encourage your child to count on in ones from one number to the next. For example, for 5 + 2 + 3: *5 and 2 is... 6, 7. Then, 7 and 3 is... 8, 9, 10.* If your child finds this difficult provide ten counters which they can use to represent their numbers. Suggest that they put the ten counters into three piles and then count on to make the sums. Challenge your child to find more examples of three numbers which total 10.

Name:

Stamps

- There are 1p, 2p and 4p stamps.
- Write some stamps onto each parcel to make the total.

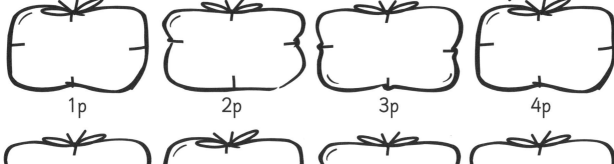

1p   2p   3p   4p

5p   6p   7p   8p

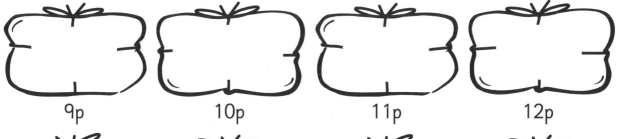

9p   10p   11p   12p

13p   14p   15p   16p

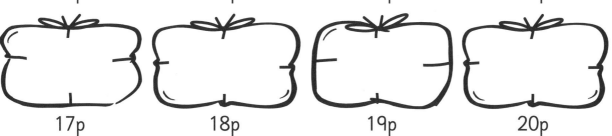

17p   18p   19p   20p

Dear Helper,

This activity helps your child to solve problems. You may find it helpful to cut out some 'stamps' for 1p, 2p and 4p. Encourage your child to decide which stamp or stamps are needed to make the price for each parcel. If your child finds this difficult, discuss how the price for each parcel is 1p more than the previous one. Discuss which combination of stamps would be best, encouraging your child to count on in ones from the value of each stamp to the next. Challenge your child to find different solutions for each parcel and to decide which one would use the least number of stamps.

Food comparison

- Find a tin of baked beans, a packet of cereal and a potato.
- Compare their weight by holding them.
- Draw them in order from lightest to heaviest.

Lightest   Heaviest

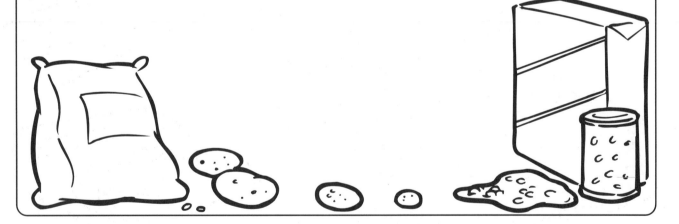

Dear Helper,

This activity helps your child to understand that things have weight. Ask your child to take two items, hold one in each hand and compare them for weight. Discuss which is heavier/lighter. Now compare both of these with the third item. Ask your child to put the items in order. If your child finds this difficult, check that they are comparing their weight and not what they see. A large item is not necessarily heavier than a smaller one. Challenge your child to compare four or five things from the store cupboard and order them by weight.

Weighing

- Decide what goes with each weighing machine.
- Join the pairs together.

Dear Helper,

This activity helps your child to make sensible choices of weighing machines when weighing an item. Encourage your child to talk about each item to be weighed and how they would weigh it. If your child finds this difficult, discuss how heavy they think the item will be and which weighing machine would be best for this. Challenge your child to think of further suggestions for what could be weighed on each machine.

Name:

About the same

- Choose some things which you think weigh about the same as your reading book.
- Compare them by holding them.
- Fill in the chart.

I chose:	✓ It was about the same weight as my book.	✓ It was heavier than my book.	✓ It was lighter than my book.

Dear Helper,

This activity helps your child to make comparisons of weight by holding. As well as your child's reading book they will need to find other things to compare. Ask your child to hold the book in one hand and, for example, a pencil case in the other. Ask: *Do they weigh about the same? Which one is heavier/lighter?* Encourage your child to find things which weigh about the same as their book. If your child finds this hard, check that they are comparing what is felt, not what is seen, by asking your child to close their eyes. Challenge your child to find as many things as possible which weigh about the same as a different sized book.

Name:

Shape pattern

- Cut out these shapes.

- Make a pattern with them.

- Stick your pattern on to some more paper.

- Colour it in.

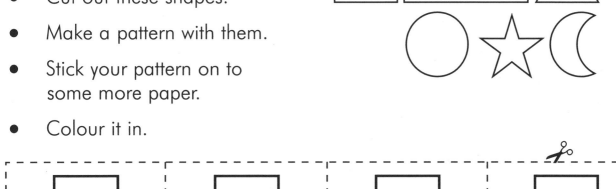

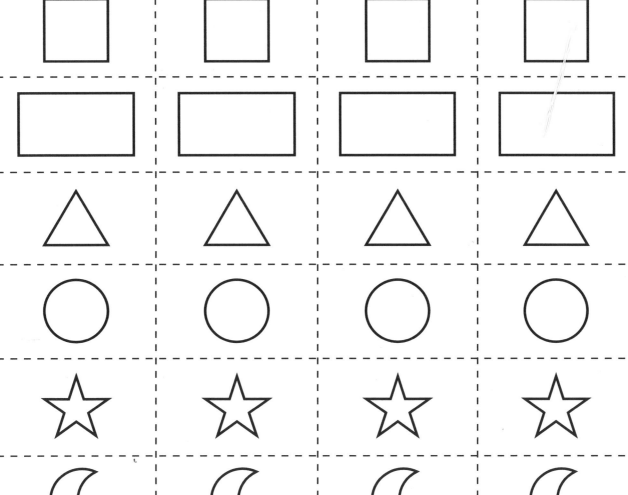

Dear Helper,

This activity is to help your child to recognise the properties of shapes and how they can be used to make a pattern. Your child will need a safe pair of scissors, adhesive such as a child-safe glue stick and some more paper to stick the shapes on to. Ask your child to name the shapes provided and to tell you about them, such as how many sides each has and whether it has curved or straight sides. If your child finds this difficult, encourage them to trace the edge of the shape with their finger to feel if the sides are straight or curved. Challenge your child to move the shapes about to make several patterns before deciding upon a favourite to stick on to paper.

Name:

Half a shape

- Fold the paper along the line.

- Cut out the shape.

- Open it up.

- What shape do you have?

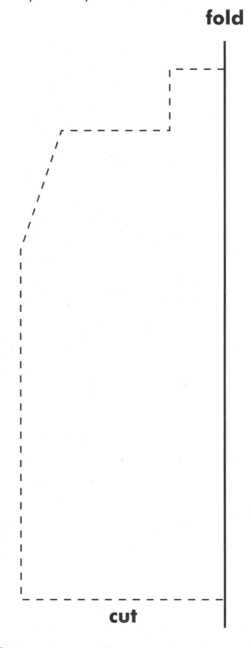

fold

cut

Dear Helper,

This activity helps your child begin to understand about 'symmetry'. Help your child to fold the paper along the line. Discuss what they can see and what shape they think will emerge after cutting. If your child finds this difficult, hold a mirror along the fold line and ask them to look at the shape and its reflection. Ask your child to cut out the shape, being careful not to cut along the fold line. Talk about what looks the same in the two parts. Challenge your child to draw half a shape, fold the paper, cut it out and check that they have the whole shape that was expected.

Name:

Jigsaw

- Cut out the jigsaw.

- Mix up the pieces.

- Make the jigsaw.

Dear Helper,

Jigsaw puzzles help your child to solve shape problems. Talk about the picture on this jigsaw, where the objects are and what shapes they have. Your child will need a safe pair of scissors in order to cut it out. Then ask your child to mix the pieces up. If your child finds it hard to reassemble the jigsaw, talk about which pieces make up an edge. Challenge your child to cut up an old greetings card, without looking at the picture, then to reassemble it into a picture.

NUMBERS AND THE NUMBER SYSTEM

COUNTING AND NUMBER PROPERTIES

Odd or even snap

You will need: some playing cards
with the picture cards removed.

- Shuffle the rest of the cards together.

- Share the cards between the two players.

- Take turns to turn over a card and make two piles of cards.
  If the top card on both piles is odd say: *Odd snap!*
  If the top card on both piles is even say: *Even snap!*
  If you are right, take both piles of cards.

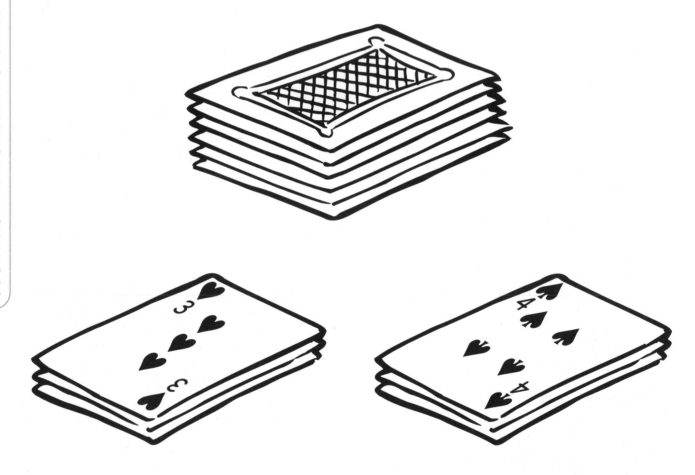

The winner is the one with all the cards at the end of the game.

Dear Helper,

This activity helps your child to recognise odd and even numbers. If your child finds the game hard, put some cards in number order and count along in twos: 1, 3, 5, 7, 9 and explain that these are odd numbers. Repeat for the even numbers: 2, 4, 6, 8, 10. Challenge your child to play the game quickly so that there is little thinking time.

PHOTOCOPIABLE

Name:

Counting pictures

- Count the pictures.

- Write down how many there are.

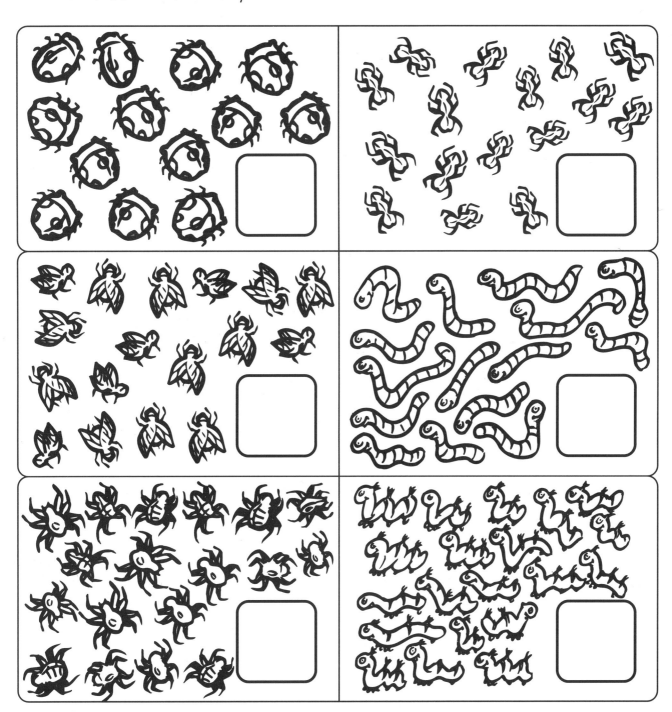

Dear Helper,

It is important for your child to be able to count accurately. Challenge your child to estimate how many pictures there are before counting them. Encourage your child to touch each picture lightly with a pencil and to mark which items have been counted so that they can see which have still to be counted. If your child finds this activity difficult put out some counters, pennies or buttons and ask them to move each as it is counted so that they can see which have been recorded.

Adding

It doesn't matter which order you add up the numbers.
The answer will always be the same.
$5 + 4 = 9$ and $4 + 5 = 9$!

- Write three more pairs of add sums to show this.

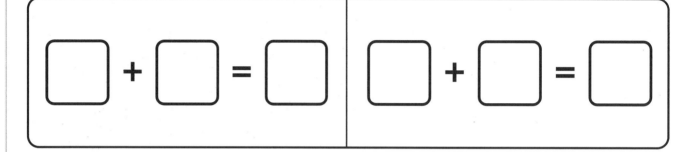

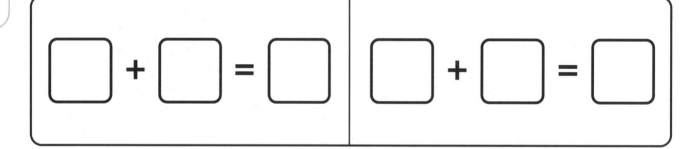

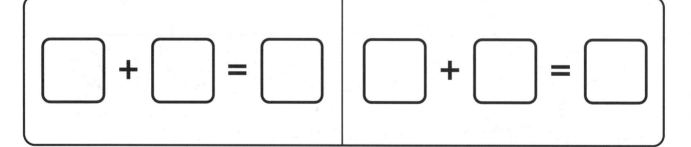

Dear Helper,

This activity helps your child to understand the general statement about addition (at the top of the page) and to find sums which fit it. Begin by asking your child to write down an addition sum. Ask them to write it again with the numbers in a different order. For example, $3 + 4 = 7$ and $4 + 3 = 7$. Ask them to write some more sums in the same way. If your child finds this difficult, write another example using numbers that total 10 or less. Challenge your child to try this sum where three numbers are added: *Is it still true?* $(3 + 4 + 5 = 12; 4 + 5 + 3 = 12; 5 + 3 + 4 = 12....)$

Name:

Sports day

- Look at the children in the pictures.
  Who is first?
  Who is last?
  Where is Jon?

Dear Helper,

This activity helps your child to understand and use the language of ordering. Look at the picture together. Ask: *Who is first? Who is last? Where is Jon?* Repeat this for the other children in the race. If your child finds this hard, encourage them to count the children by pointing at them in order starting with the winner. Challenge your child to put some coins in the order that you say. Put out five coins: a 1p, 2p, 5p, 10p and 20p coin. Say: *Put the 5p first. Put the 2p after the 10p....*

Name:

Comparing and ordering numbers

Choose from these numbers.

2   6   9   13   18

- Write a number in the **Less** box.

- Write a number in the **More** box.

- Now choose your own number to go in between the two numbers.

- Write it in the middle box.

Less   **More**

Dear Helper,

This activity helps your child to compare and order numbers. Ask your child to choose their two numbers and write the lower number in the 'Less' box and the higher number in the 'More' box. If your child finds this difficult, count aloud from one number to the next so that that they are clear about the ordering of the numbers. Now ask: *What number could go between?* Challenge your child to find different solutions for the number between each pair of numbers.

Addition patterns for 13

• Continue the addition pattern for 13.

2 + 11 = 13
1 + 12 = 13
0 + 13 = 13

Dear Helper,

This activity helps your child to see patterns in addition and to use this to help them to find more answers.
Ask: *What comes next in the pattern?* Talk together about how as one number increases by 1 each time,
the other number decreases by 1. If your child finds this difficult, complete the next two or three sums
together then encourage your child to try one alone. Further challenge your child by asking them to write
the addition pattern for 14 in the same way on the back of the sheet.

Name:

Addition grid

You will need: two counters, pennies or buttons.

- Throw the counters on to the grid.

- Write an addition sum using the numbers they land on.

- Work out the total and write it in the box.

- Do this six times.

1	2	3	4	5
6	7	8	9	10

☐ + ☐ = ☐   ☐ + ☐ = ☐

☐ + ☐ = ☐   ☐ + ☐ = ☐

☐ + ☐ = ☐   ☐ + ☐ = ☐

Dear Helper,

To complete this activity, encourage your child to write the larger number first, then count on in ones to find the total. For example, for the numbers 4 and 9, ask your child to start from the 9 and then count on: *10, 11, 12, 13. So 4 add 9 is 13*. If your child finds this difficult, count on together, keeping a check of how many have been counted by using your fingers. Challenge your child further to complete at least ten sums.

Trio cards

- Cut out the trio cards.

- Say all four facts for each card.
  For example, for this 3, 4, 7 card,
  you would say: 3 + 4 = 7; 4 + 3 = 7; 7 − 3 = 4; 7 - 4 = 3.

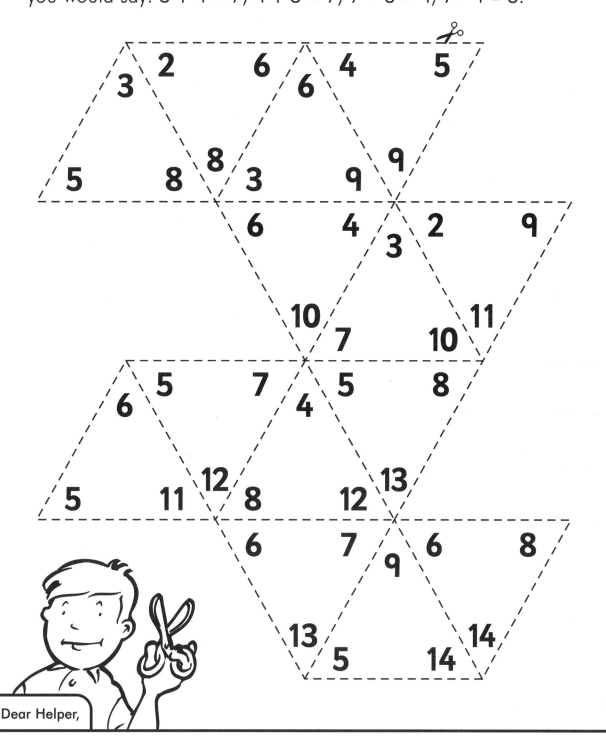

Dear Helper,

Your child needs to realise that if an addition fact is found then the related subtraction fact can also be found. For example, for the numbers 3, 5 and 8: 3 + 5 = 8, so 5 + 3 = 8; but also 8 − 3 = 5, and 8 − 5 = 3. Ask your child to choose a trio card and use the numbers on it to say the four related addition and subtraction facts. If they find this difficult, say one of the facts and encourage your child to find the others. Challenge your child to make up their own trio fact cards.

Three number addition

- Throw three counters, pennies or buttons on to the grid.

- Write the numbers they land on in the boxes.

- Add the numbers.

- Write the total.

1	3	5
2	4	6

- Do four more sums like this.

☐ + ☐ + ☐ = ☐

☐ + ☐ + ☐ = ☐

☐ + ☐ + ☐ = ☐

☐ + ☐ + ☐ = ☐

☐ + ☐ + ☐ = ☐

Dear Helper,

This activity will encourage your child to use their mental methods to add three small numbers. Ask your child to explain their adding strategy. Your child might say: *I put the largest number first; ...look for doubles; ...combine pairs of numbers to make 10* and so on. If your child finds this hard and is short of ideas, encourage them to count on in ones from the largest number. Challenge your child to add up four numbers.

Name:

Favourite outings

Which is your favourite outing?

- Put a tick in its column.
- Ask your family to answer the question.
- Put ticks in the columns for them.

Going swimming	Going to the cinema	Going out for a meal	Going to the park	Going to the seaside	Visiting family

Dear Helper,

In this activity your child is collecting and recording information. Discuss their favourite outing from the list on the chart. Now get your child to ask other family members which is their favourite outing. When some 'data' has been collected, ask your child questions such as: *Which is the most/least popular outing? How many people like going to the seaside best? How many more people like... than... ?* Challenge your child further by asking them to think of other things to ask the family and to make their own chart.

89

Marble grab

Ask your family and friends to help.

- Put some marbles in a tub.

- Ask each person to pick up a handful of marbles.

- Count and write down how many they picked up.

You try first.

Name	Number of marbles

Dear Helper,

In this activity your child is practising organising data in a list. If you don't have marbles, buttons or dried pasta shapes, for example, will do. You might like to ask questions such as: *Who held the least/most? Who held more than you? How many more?* To help your child, discuss what goes into each column of the list. Encourage them to touch and move each marble/button/piece of pasta as it is counted, so that they know which have been counted already and which are still to be counted.

Name:

Time sheet

- Look at the time on each clock.
- Draw a picture of what you do at that time.

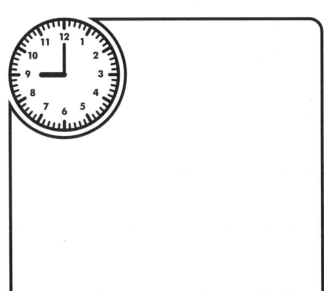

Dear Helper,

This activity helps your child to tell the time and to relate the time to what they do in the day. Look at the times on the clocks together. Ask your child to say what time each clock says and to decide what they do at that time. If your child finds this hard, talk about the day and what your child has done and at what times. If your child wishes they can write a sentence under each picture to explain what they are doing. Challenge your child to think of other things that they do every day and to draw them with their own clock faces to record the time when they are done. Your child could use the back of this sheet for their drawings.

Name:

Days of the week

This activity is about the days of the week.

- Write the answers to the questions.

What day is it today?

_____

What day was it yesterday?

_____

What day will it be tomorrow?

_____

What is the day after Friday?

_____

On which days do you go to school?

_____

_____

_____

Sunday

Monday

Tuesday

Wednesday

Thursday

Friday

Saturday

Dear Helper,

This activity is to help your child to know the days of the week in order and to read and write the names of the days. Ask your child to say the days of the week in order, starting with Sunday. Read the questions together and then ask your child to find the day or days for each answer. Ask further questions such as: *On which day will we go to...? What did you do (say) two days ago? What day was that?*

Name:

Hand span measure

Look around you at home.

- Find some things at home which you think are about as long as your hand span.

- Find some things which you think are about as long as 2 hand spans.

- Find some things which you think are about as long as 3 hand spans.

- Draw pictures to show what you found.

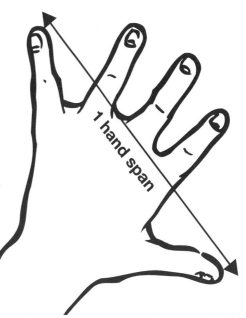

1 hand span

About as long as 1 hand span	About as long as 2 hand spans	About as long as 3 hand spans

Dear Helper,

This activity will help your child to estimate and measure using non-standard units. Encourage your child to estimate first by making a good guess of things which will be about the correct length. If your child finds this hard, ask them to compare physically their hand span with things at home. Talk about how close the estimate was and whether it was just over or just under. Challenge your child to find things about as long as 4, 5 or 6 hand spans.

PHOTOCOPIABLE

Name:

About a kilogram

Ask an adult to help you.

- Fill a litre bottle with water and put the top on.

- Your bottle of water weighs about a kilogram (1kg).

- Use it to compare the weight of things at home.

- Find things which weigh about 1kg.

- Draw pictures of them.

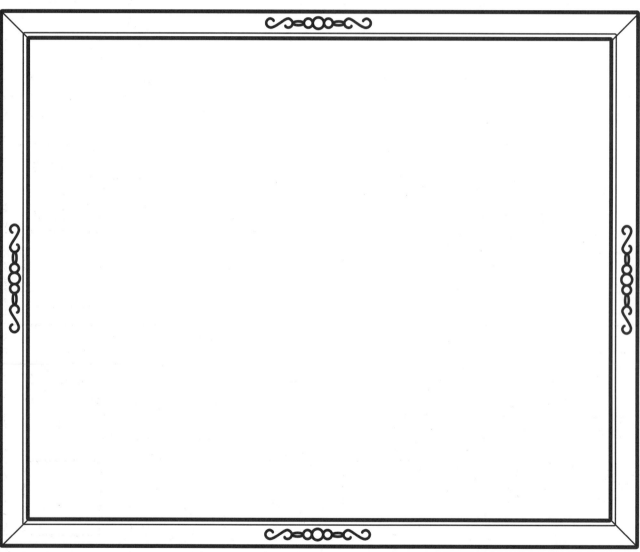

Dear Helper,

It is a fascinating fact that 1 litre of water weighs 1kg. In this activity, with your help, your child is going to estimate weights of 1kg. Things that will weigh about 1kg include a standard bag of sugar or flour. Ask your child to hold the bottle and to feel its weight and then to hold one of the other items that they have found. For each item, ask: *Do they feel about the same? Does it weigh more/less?* Challenge your child to make a half kilogram weight, using a half litre (500ml) bottle and filling it with water, and using it to find items which weigh about ½kg (or 500g).

Name:

Counting many shapes

- Point to the pictures and count how many shapes there are.
- Write how many in each box.

Dear Helper,

This activity helps your child to count items by pointing, but not touching. For each one, check that your child has counted all of the pictures. If your child finds this hard, ask them to touch each picture as it is counted very lightly with a pencil to leave a small mark. This will help your child to see which pictures have been counted and which still need to be counted. Challenge your child by taking a handful of counters or pennies and spreading them out randomly on the table. Ask your child to count the items without touching them.

Name:

What comes next?

- Continue the number patterns.

- Write what comes next on to the caterpillars.

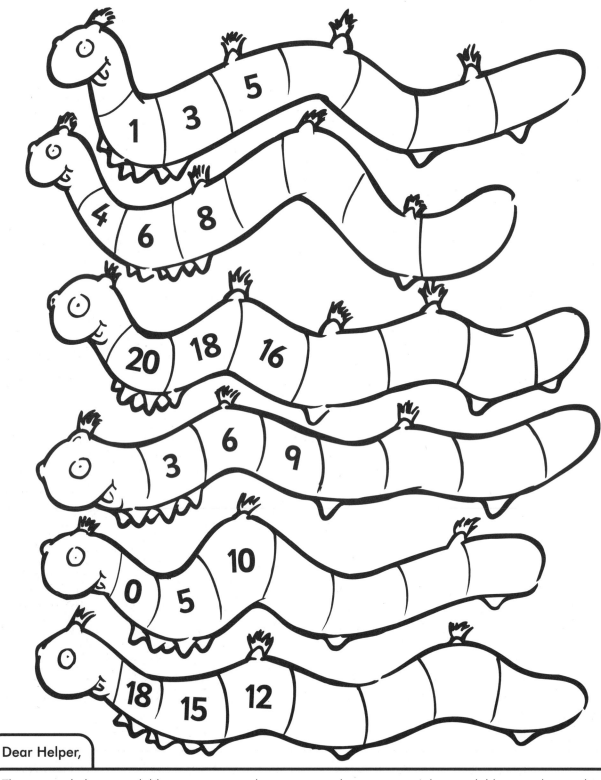

Dear Helper,

This activity helps your child to recognise and continue number patterns. Ask your child to say the numbers in the first caterpillar and then to say what comes next, and next. If your child finds this hard, ask questions such as: *Are these odd or even numbers? By how many does the pattern go up (or down) each time?* Then count together to the next number in the pattern. Challenge your child to write some more number patterns of their own and to explain these to you.

Name:

Missing numbers

- Choose two of the numbers below.

- Write them in the boxes, in order.

- Now write any two numbers which will fit between them, in order.

- Repeat this four more times.

2   5   9   13   18

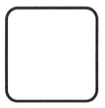

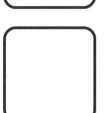

Dear Helper,

This activity will help your child to compare numbers by size and order them. Ask your child: *Which is the smallest number here? Which is the largest?* Now ask them to choose two of the given numbers and any two more which will fit between them. So if they choose 2 and 13, they could choose any two numbers from 3 to 12 to fit between. If your child finds this hard, suggest that they write all the numbers from 2 to 18 in order, so that they can see the position of all the numbers in the order. Challenge your child to make up some more number orders, choosing any numbers.

Name:

Counter moves

You will need: four different coloured counters and a dice.

- Roll the dice and move the first counter the number of your score.

- Roll the dice again and move the second counter.

- Now roll the dice and move the third counter.

- Now roll the dice and move the fourth counter.

- Repeat this until one of the counters gets to the finish line.

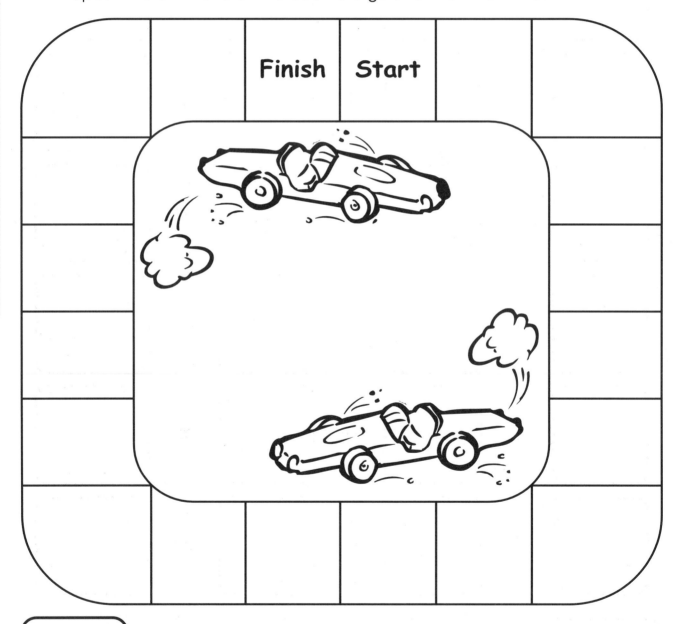

Finish **Start**

Dear Helper,

This activity helps your child to understand about number order. Play the game together. After each counter moves, ask questions such as: *Which counter is winning? Which is last? Which one is second/third?* If your child finds this hard, point to the order of the counters and discuss which one is closest to winning. The game can be played with four players each moving just one counter.

Name:

Card add

Use all the Ace to 6 cards from some playing cards.

- Take three cards.
- Write an add sum and the answer.
- Repeat this five times.

UNDERSTANDING + AND –

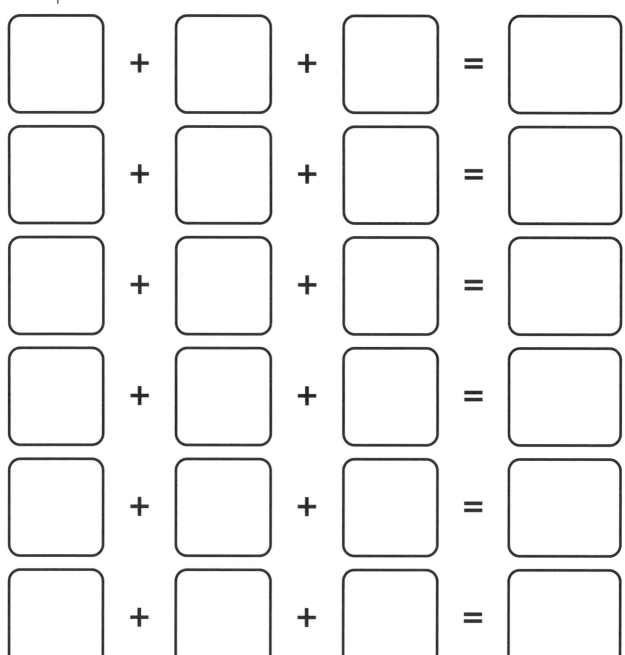

Dear Helper,

This activity helps your child to understand that more than two numbers can be added together. For each sum ask your child: *How did you work that out?* If your child finds this difficult, suggest that they start with the largest number and then count on in ones to add the next. Repeat for the next number. Challenge your child to use the playing cards 3 to 8 to make more sums.

100 MATHS HOMEWORK ACTIVITIES • YEAR 1 TERM 3

MENTAL CALCULATIONS · CALCULATIONS

Bridging 10

You will need: a counter.

- Toss the counter on to the number grid.

- Add the number that the counter falls on to 8.

- Write an addition sum for your numbers.

- Repeat this five more times.

1	2	3
4	5	6
7	8	9

Dear Helper,

This activity helps your child to add numbers where the total crosses 10. This strategy is called 'bridging 10'. For 8 + 6, ask your child to break this down to make a 10: 8 + 6 = 8 + 2 + 4 = 10 + 4 = 14. If your child finds this hard, suggest that they count on in ones to make the 10, then in ones again. Challenge your child to add their grid number to 18, so that they bridge 20 in the same way: 18 + 6 = 18 + 2 + 4 = 20 + 4 = 24.

PHOTOCOPIABLE

Name:

Change from 20p

- Choose two things to buy.
- Work out the total cost and write it in the chart.
- Work out the change from 20p and write it in the chart.
- Do this three more times.

I chose	Total	Change from 20p

Dear Helper,

This activity helps your child to find total cost and give change from 20p. If your child finds this hard use some real money to total the cost of two items and then to count out the change from 20p. Challenge them to find more totals and change from 20p.

Name:

Total 14

- Choose two numbers which total 14.

- Write them in the boxes.

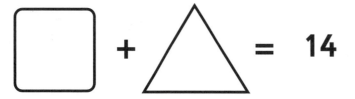

- Now find five more pairs of numbers from the grid which total 14.

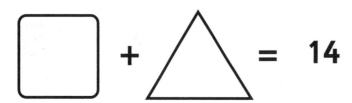

1	8
2	9
3	10
4	11
5	12
6	13
7	14

Dear Helper,

This activity helps your child to use the mental strategy for bridging 10. When adding 6 and 8 encourage your child to take two mental steps: $6 + 8 = 6 + 4 + 4 = 10 + 4 = 14$. If your child finds this hard, count on in ones. Alternatively, make a number line for the numbers 0 to 14 and suggest that your child uses this to help. Challenge your child to use the numbers 1 to 20 and to add two numbers each time to make totals of 16.

Name:

Addition sums

- Finish these sums.

 **+** **6** **=** **15**

9 **+** **=** **15**

8 **+**  **=** **15**

 **+** **7** **=** **15**

 +  **=** **15**

 + **=** **15**

Dear Helper,

This activity helps your child to use the mental strategy for bridging 10 to complete these sums. For example, for 9 + 6: 9 + 1 + 5 = 10 + 5 = 15. If your child finds the work difficult, suggest that they draw a number line from 0 to 16 and counts along that to help. Challenge your child to find more ways of totalling 15, adding two or three numbers. They can write their ideas on the back of this sheet.

Name:

Subtraction sums

- Finish these subtraction sums.
- Use different numbers to complete each one.

16   –      =

16   –      =

16   –      =

16   –   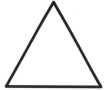   =

16   –      =

16   –      =

Dear Helper,

This activity helps your child to use their knowledge of number facts to complete these subtraction sums. If your child finds these difficult, draw a number line from 0 to 16 and suggest that your child uses this to help them by counting on from any smaller number to 16: start at 9, count on 7. This gives $16 - 7 = 9$; and $16 - 9 = 7$. Challenge your child to find more than six examples, writing further ideas on the back of this sheet.

Name:

Total 20p

You will need: some coins to help you.

- Find different ways to make 20p exactly.

- Draw the coins you used to show what you did.

- Find five different ways.

Dear Helper,

This activity helps your child to recognise that there are different ways of making the same total of money. Begin by counting out some coins into your child's hand and ask: *How much is that? How much more do we need to make 20p?* Now ask your child to count some coins into your hands to make 20p. Encourage them to use the 'shopkeeper's method' of counting on: *10p and 5p makes 15p and 5p more makes 20p.* Suggest that they draw around the coins and writes the value in the centre of each one to record what they did. Challenge your child to find more than five ways of doing this.

Name:

Water fun

Find some cups, jugs and other kitchen containers.

- How many cups of water do you think the jug will hold?

  I think the jug will hold [ ] cups of water.

- Fill it and find out.

  I used [ ] cups to fill the jug.

- Was that a good estimate?

- Now use some other things to fill the jug.

  I used [ ] _____ to fill the jug.

  I used [ ] _____ to fill the jug.

- Which was best to use?

  The _____ was the best thing to choose

  to fill the jug.

Dear Helper,

This activity helps your child to experience measuring capacity. This can be a messy activity, so decide whether it might be better to carry this out in the bath at bath time. Talk with your child about their estimate and encourage them to make sensible guesses then before checking by pouring. Other containers such as empty yogurt pots and margarine tubs can be used, filled with spoonfuls of water. Challenge your child to suggest other containers that could be used and to estimate how many cups or spoonfuls of water they will hold. Check by measuring.

Name: _____

Capacity comparison

- Look at the pictures of the containers.
- Write the answers to the questions as an addition or subtraction.

The jug holds
7 cupfuls.

The teapot holds
6 cupfuls.

The saucepan holds 9
cupfuls.

How much more does the
jug hold than the teapot?   _____

How many cupfuls
will two jugs hold?   _____

How much more does the
saucepan hold than the teapot?   _____

How much do the jug and
the teapot hold together?   _____

Dear Helper,

This activity helps your child to solve number problems set in measuring contexts. Read the questions with your child and ask them to solve them and to write the answer as a sum. If your child finds this difficult, talk about the type of sum that is needed to answer the question. Challenge your child to make up some more questions about the jug, teapot and saucepan.

Name:

Picture these

Look around you at home.

- Find two things that will **turn** and draw them.
- Find two things that will **roll** and draw them.
- Now find two things that will **slide** and draw them.
- Try to find some things that will **slide and roll** and draw them.

Things that turn	Things that slide
Things that roll	**Things that slide and roll**

Dear Helper,

This activity helps your child to understand about position, direction and movement. Look around the house together to find things that will fit each box. For example, the door handle turns; the clock hands turn. If your child finds this difficult, talk about how the items move. Challenge your child to find more items for each group.

Name:

Colour pattern

- Continue each pattern down the page.
- Colour each pattern so that it repeats.

 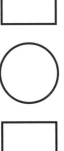 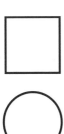  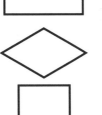 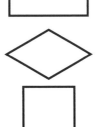   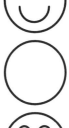

Dear Helper,

This activity helps your child to recognise, copy and continue patterns. If your child finds this difficult, 'say' the pattern beginning together and ask: *What comes next? Now what comes next?* Challenge your child to make up their own repeating patterns on the back of the sheet and to colour these so that they still repeat.

Find the way home

- Help Abdul to find his way home from school.

- Draw in a route.

- How many different ways can you find?

Dear Helper,

This activity helps your child to understand about position, direction and movement. Talk about possible ways home on the sheet. Encourage your child to explain the route, using language such as: *turn left; go straight on; turn right*. If your child finds this hard, ask them to show with their hands which way to move and say the words to describe the movement. Challenge your child to draw their route home from school.

Name:

Number pattern board game

You will need: a friend to play with, a dice and some counters.

- Toss a counter onto the 2, 3 and 5 circle.
  This will tell you whether to count in 2s, 3s or 5s.

- Now roll the dice.
  This will tell you how many steps to move.

- As you move your counter, one step at a
  time, count in 2s, 3s or 5s. The first one
  to finish wins.

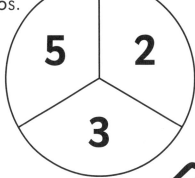

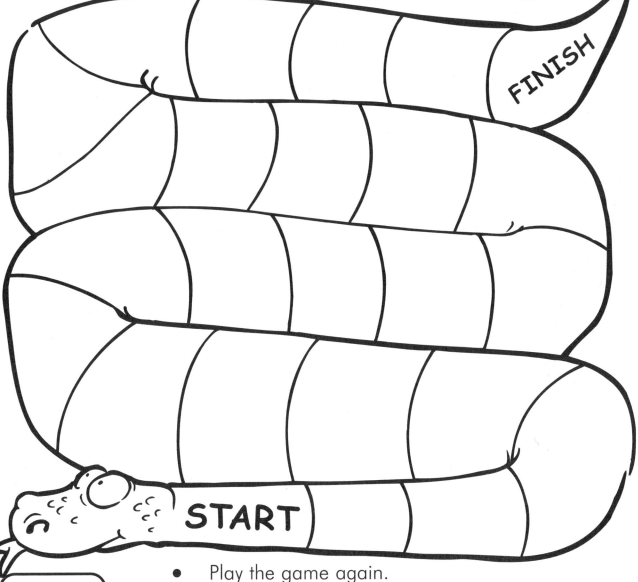

- Play the game again.

Dear Helper,

This game helps your child to count in 2s, 3s and 5s. Play the game together. If your child finds the counting difficult, say the number pattern together until they are more confident with this. Play the game through a number of times over a few days until your child is confident. Challenge your child to count in odd numbers or even numbers for counting in 2s.

Number patterns

- Write some number patterns.

- Make a pattern with just even numbers.

- Make a pattern that includes the number 17.

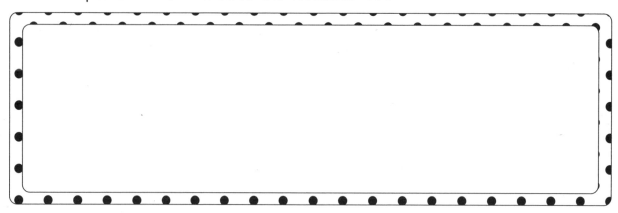

- Make a pattern that includes the number 9.

Dear Helper,

This activity helps your child to recognise and create number patterns. Begin by talking about even numbers and ask your child to say some even numbers: 2, 4, 6, 8... . For the pattern that includes the number 17, ask them what sort of number pattern this might appear in (for example, counting in tens starting on 7; odd numbers...). For the pattern with 9, ask similar questions. When your child has written a pattern ask them to explain it to you. Challenge your child to create other number patterns and to explain these to you.

COUNTING AND NUMBER PROPERTIES | **NUMBERS AND THE NUMBER SYSTEM**

PHOTOCOPIABLE

Name:

Making 19

I can make 19 by adding three numbers.
How can I do this?

- Write some sums to show this.

Dear Helper,

This activity helps your child to investigate a general statement about numbers and find examples that satisfy it. Ask your child to explain the statement: *I can make 19 by adding three numbers.* Encourage them to find some examples of adding three numbers to show that this is true. If your child finds this hard, draw a number line from 0 to 19 to help them by counting along it. Challenge your child to find at least six sums which show three numbers added together which total 19.

NUMBERS AND THE NUMBER SYSTEM

PLACE VALUE AND ORDERING

Ordering to 20

You will need: a partner for this game.
· Use playing cards Ace to 10.

- Shuffle the cards and place them face down on the table.

- Take five cards each and put them out in front of you in the order that they come off the pile.

   The idea of the game is to have all five cards in front of you in order, from lowest to highest value.

- Take turns to take another card and decide whether to change it for one of your cards.

- Keep doing this until all your cards are in order.
   The first one to order all their cards is the winner.

I will change the 4 card for the 8 so that the last three cards are in order.

Dear Helper,

This game helps your child to compare and order numbers. The game can be played by one person, but it is more fun if two or more people play it! If your child finds it hard, ask them about their cards and which ones need to be changed. As your child takes each new card talk about where the card might fit, or whether it would be better to discard it. Challenge your child to play this game with six cards to be ordered.

Counter count

You will need: some counters for this activity.

- Take a handful of counters.
- Estimate how many there are and write this in the chart.
- Now count how many counters you had and write this in the chart.
- Put a tick in the box which describes your estimate.
- Repeat this activity five more times.

My estimate	My count	My estimate was		
		not enough ✓	about right ✓	too many ✓

Dear Helper,

This activity helps your child to make more accurate estimates of 'how many'. You can use counters, small bricks or larger coins for this activity. If your child finds it hard to estimate, encourage them to look carefully at how many there are (without counting). The estimation should become more accurate with practice. Your child could repeat the activity with other family members.

Name:

Where does it fit?

- Write the numbers in order on to the trucks starting with the smallest number.

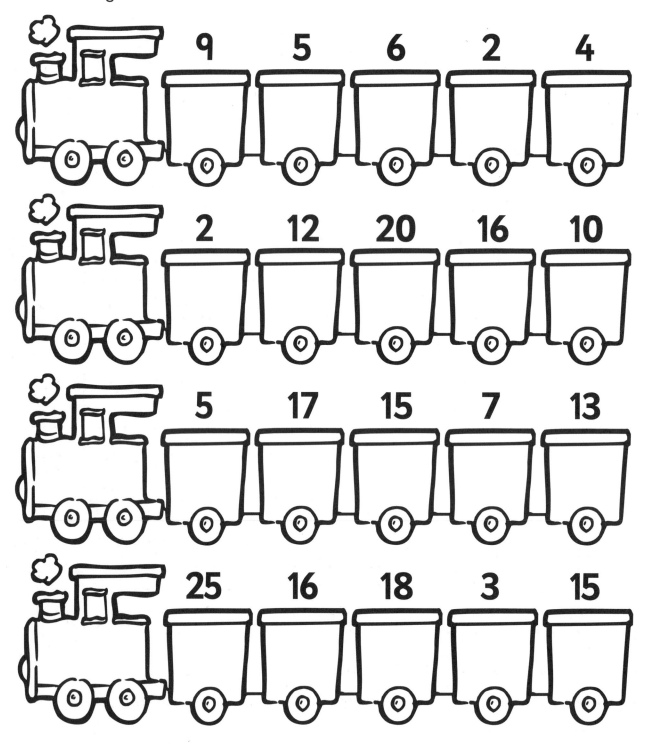

9   5   6   2   4

2   12   20   16   10

5   17   15   7   13

25   16   18   3   15

Dear Helper,

This activity helps your child to order numbers. Begin by talking about the first set of numbers. Ask your child which is the smallest number and then which is the biggest number. Encourage them to say which comes next after the smallest and so on. Challenge your child to order some more numbers from small to large.

Number cover up

You will need: some counters, paper and a pencil. Play this game with a friend.

1   Each person tosses a counter on to the spinner once.

2   Note down the two numbers.

3   Add those two numbers together.

That gives you the total you need to make.

4   Choose numbers from the grid to make a number sentence with that total.

5   Record the number sentence.

6   Cover the numbers you chose from the grid with counters as you use them.

1	2	3	4	5
6	7	8	9	10
11	12	13	14	15
16	17	18	19	20

Record like this:

First number	Second number	Total to make	Number sentence
4 + 9 = 13			10 + 3 = 13

You can only use a grid number once.

The winner is the one who makes the most sentences.

Dear Helper,

This activity helps your child to use their mental strategies to solve addition and subtraction problems. Play the game together. If your child finds it hard, draw a number line from 0 to 20 and encourage them to count along and back to find ways of making a given total. Your child can add two or three numbers together to make a total. Challenge your child to consider adding and subtracting in one calculation. For example, to make a total of 10, this could be 20 − 13 + 3. If they need more writing space, tell your child to use the back of this page.

CALCULATIONS

UNDERSTANDING + AND −

Box add

- Choose two numbers to make an add sum with a total which is more than 10.

| 4 | 5 | 6 | 7 | 8 | 9 |

- Write your sum.

- Repeat this five times.

Dear Helper,

This activity helps your child to add numbers where the total crosses 10. This is called 'bridging 10'. Encourage your child to take two mental steps: $9 + 7 = 9 + 1 + 6 = 10 + 6 = 16$. If your child finds this hard, encourage them to count on in ones to make 10, then count on in ones for the remaining amount. Challenge your child to make sums which cross 20 using 4, 5, 6, 7, 8, 9 and 14, 15, 16, 17, 18, 19.

Totals

- Choose two numbers to make a total between 18 and 25.
- Write a number sentence.
- Repeat this five times.

1	2	3	4	5	6	7	8	9	10
11	12	13	14	15	16	17	18	19	20

Dear Helper,

This activity helps your child to add two numbers with a total that may cross the 20 boundary. Encourage your child to use a two-step mental strategy: $14 + 8 = 14 + 6 + 2 = 20 + 2 = 22$. If your child finds this hard, encourage them to count on in ones: *14 + 6 is 15, 16, 17, 18, 19, 20*. Then they can count on in ones to find the final total: *21, 22. So 14 + 8 is 22.* Challenge your child to make totals using the numbers which are greater than 25.

Name:

Giving change

You will need: some coins and a friend to help you.

- Take turns to be the shopkeeper and the customer.

- The customer chooses two things to buy which must cost 20p or less in total.

- The shopkeeper counts out the change from 20p.

5p

11p

7p

9p

6p

10p

8p

14p

12p

13p

15p

Dear Helper,

This activity helps your child to total prices and work out change from 20p. Take it in turns to be the customer and the shopkeeper. Your child will find it helpful to use coins to count out the change. If your child finds this hard, encourage them to count out the change using the 'shopkeeper's method'. For a total of 14p, the change could be counted out as: *1p makes 15p, and 5p makes 20p. That's 6p change.* Challenge your child to buy three items that cost 20p or less in total.

Name:

Totalling 19

- Choose two numbers each time to make a total of 19.

- Write the sum in the recording space.

- Repeat this five times.

1	2	3	4	5	6	7	8	9	10
11	12	13	14	15	16	17	18	19	

Dear Helper,

This activity helps your child to solve word problems. Begin by asking your child which two numbers they think might total 19. Now encourage them to use mental strategies to check their estimate. This could be counting on in ones, or using facts that are already known, such as if 5 + 4 = 9, then 15 + 4 = 19. If your child finds this hard, encourage them to count on in ones from the larger number. Challenge your child to find ten possible solutions, by totalling two or three numbers each time.

Name:

Paying 18p

You will need: some coins.

- Choose some coins that total 18p.

- Draw around each coin and write its value inside.

- Find four more ways of making 18p and record them.

- Tick the way that uses the least number of coins.

Dear Helper,

This activity helps your child to recognise that it is possible to pay the same amount of money in different ways. Provide some coins for your child to use and encourage them to count the coins using the 'shopkeeper's method': *10p and 5p is 15p, and 2p is 17p and 1p is 18p*. If your child finds this difficult, count the coins into their hands and then ask them to do the same for you. Talk about how using the least number of coins may be more convenient. Challenge your child to find seven different ways of making 18p.

Name:

Measuring capacity

- Decide how you would measure the capacity of each container.
- Join each container to the unit you would use.

Containers   **Units**

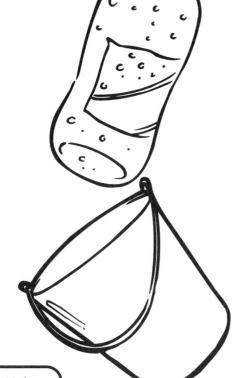

Dear Helper,

This activity helps your child to make decisions about suitable units for measuring capacity. Talk about the objects on the sheet. If you have some of these at home, look at them together and discuss how large each is and which unit would be best to fill it. Challenge your child to find other containers that could be filled. Ask them to draw and then join the picture to the appropriate unit.

Time order

- Join the picture to its clock.

MEASURES MEASURES, SHAPE AND SPACE

Dear Helper,

This activity helps your child to tell the time and to recognise at what time of day certain events happen. It may help to have a clock which can be set to the times on the sheet. If your child finds this hard, encourage them to say what is happening in each picture and at what sort of time of day that would occur. Your child can then match this to the nearest time shown on a clock. Challenge your child to think of other things that they do during the day and to say what time these thing occur.

100 MATHS HOMEWORK ACTIVITIES • YEAR 1 TERM 3

Name: _____

The week and the seasons

- Write the answers to the questions about the days of the week.

Sunday Monday Tuesday Wednesday Thursday Friday Saturday

What day is it today? _____

What day will it be tomorrow? _____

What day was it yesterday? _____

On which days do you come to school? _____

_____

On which days do you stay at home? _____

_____

- Now look at the pictures.
  Join the name of the season to its picture.

| Spring | Summer | Autumn | Winter |

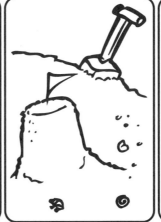

Dear Helper,

This activity helps your child to know the days of the week in order and to recognise the main features of the seasons. Say the days of the week together and then read the questions together. If your child is unsure about the answers, talk about what day it is today, what day it will be tomorrow, and so on. Encourage your child to use the days of the week printed on the sheet to help them to work out the answers. Talk about the seasons and discuss what each one is like. Discuss the typical weather for each season.

SOLVING PROBLEMS

NUMBER PROBLEMS IN MEASURES

About me

- Draw a picture of yourself.

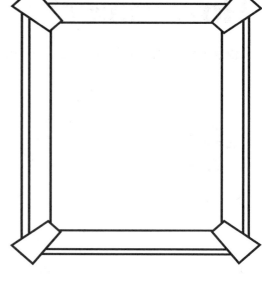

- Now finish the sentences about you.

I am ⬜ years old.

I wake up in the mornings at ⬜ o'clock.

I go to school at ⬜ o'clock.

I come home from school at ⬜ o'clock.

My favourite television programme is _____

_____

I go to bed at ⬜ o'clock.

Dear Helper,

This activity helps your child to use their knowledge about time to answer some questions. Talk about the questions together and agree that on some days there will be different answers to the questions. If your child finds this hard, use a clock to help them to see what time they do these things. Challenge your child to think of other things they do during the day and to say at what time they are done.

PHOTOCOPIABLE

Name:

How many?

You will need: some clothes pegs.

- Ask your family and friends to help.

- Ask each person to pick up as many pegs as they can.

- Now count the pegs and write the results in the chart.

Name	Number of pegs

Dear Helper,

This activity helps your child to count and record data. When your child has collected and recorded the data, ask questions such as: *Who picked the most pegs? How many? How many more did... pick up than...? Who picked up the fewest?* If your child finds this hard, talk about which are the largest and smallest numbers of pegs people picked up. Challenge your child to work out the number difference between the largest and smallest number of pegs picked up.

Name:

What can we tell?

- Look at the chart.

- Write the answers to the questions.

Our pets

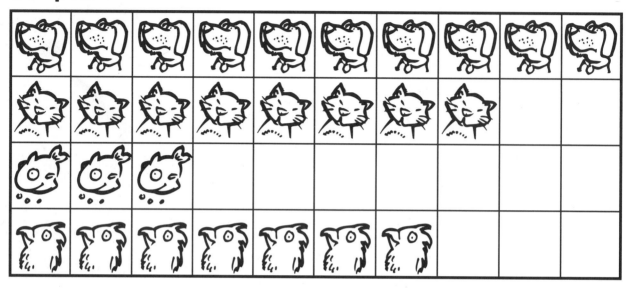

How many dogs are there?

How many cats are there?

How many more birds than fish are there?

How many fewer fish than cats are there?

Which is the most popular pet? _____

Dear Helper,

This activity helps your child to interpret the results from a graph. Talk about the graph and count how many of each pet there are. Now read the questions together. If your child finds the questions difficult to answer, compare the pictures of the pets mentioned in the question. For example, compare how many birds and fish there are and then work out the number difference between them. Challenge your child to make their own graph about pets by asking some friends what types of pets they have. They could then say which are the most popular and least popular pets.